GREEN BUSINESS:

Hope or Hoax?

First published in the UK in 1991 by
Green Books
Ford House, Hartland
Bideford, Devon EX39 6EE

Book design and typesetting by
The New Catalyst/ New Society Publishers, Canada
Cover design by Linda Wade

Printed in the United States of America
by BookCrafters, Inc., Chelsea, Michigan
Printed on partially recycled paper

British Library Cataloguing in Publication Data
Green Business: hope or hoax?
1. Great Britain. Consumption, related to Conservation
I. Plant, Christopher II. Plant, Judith
333.720941

ISBN 1 870098 34 X

Originated in the United States and Canada by:

New Society Publishers
4527 Springfield Avenue
Philadelphia, PA 19143
USA

and

New Society Publishers/New Catalyst
PO Box 189
Gabriola Island, BC VOR 1XO
CANADA

This book originated as part of *The New Catalyst Bioregional Series* which aims to inspire and stimulate the building of new, ecologically sustainable cultures in their myriad facets through presenting a broad spectrum of concerns ranging from how we view the world and act within it, through efforts at restoring damaged ecosystems or greening the cities, to the raising of a new and hopeful generation.

GREEN BUSINESS:

Hope or Hoax?

Edited by
Christopher Plant & Judith Plant

GREEN
BOOKS

Table of Contents

Acknowledgments

Grateful acknowledgment is made for permission to reprint previously published articles from the following sources:

"A Bill of Goods? Green Consuming In Perspective," by Debra Lynn Dadd and Andre Carothers, and "The Degradeable Plastics Scam." Reprinted with permission from *Greenpeace* magazine, May-June 1990: 578 Bloor Street West, Toronto, ON M6G 1K1 in Canada, and from: 1436 U Street NW, Washington DC 20009 in the U.S.A..

"Beyond Green Consumerism," by Sandy Irvine. Extracted and reprinted with permission from *Beyond Green Consumerism*, Discussion Paper No. 1, published by Friends of the Earth, U.K., September 1989: 26-28 Underwood St., London, N1 7JQ, U.K.

"The Greening of International Finance," by Brian Tokar. Excerpted and reprinted with permission from *Zeta* magazine, April 1990: The Institute for Social & Cultural Change, 116 Saint Botolph Street, Boston, MA 02115.

"The New Environmental Funds," by Susan Meeker-Lowry. Excerpted and reprinted with permission from *Catalyst: Investing in Social Change*, Fall 1989: 64 Main Street, Montpelier, VT 05602.

"Endorsing Green Capitalism," by Wayne Ellwood. Reprinted with permission from *The New Internationalist*, January 1990: 1057 McNicoll Avenue, Suite 108, Scarborough, ON M1W 3W6 in Canada, and from: P.O. Box 1143, Lewiston, NY 14092 in the U.S.A..

"Marketing The Environment," by Brian Tokar. Extracted and reprinted with permission from *Zeta* magazine, February 1990.

"Greening The Boardrooms," by Eric Mann. Reprinted with permission from *The Earth Day Wall Street Action Handbook*, April 1990: P.O. Box 1128, Old Chelsea Station, New York, NY 10011.

"Environmental Democracy is the Planet's Best Hope," by Barry Commoner. Reprinted with permission from an *Utne Reader* July/August, 1990 adaptation of an interview with Barry Commoner by Pat Stone in *Mother Earth News*, March/April 1990. *Utne Reader*: P.O. Box 1974, Marion, OH 43305. *Mother Earth News*: P.O. Box 70, Hendersonville, NC 28791.

"The Trouble With Earth Day," by Kirkpatrick Sale. Extracted and reprinted with permission from *The Nation*, April 30, 1990: 72 Fifth Avenue, New York, NY 10011.

"How Green is Your Company?" by Guy Dauncey. Extracted and reprinted with permission from *Building A Green Future*, 1989, by Guy Dauncey, available from the author at: Garden of Gaia, P.O. Box 456, Ganges BC V0S 1E0.

"50 Difficult Things You Can Do To Save The Earth," compiled by Gar Smith, was a collective effort by members of various U.S. environmental groups at the invitation of *Earth Island Journal*. Reprinted with permission. *Earth Island Journal*: 300 Broadway, Suite 28, San Francisco, CA 94133-3312.

"What Is Money?" by Alan AtKisson. Reprinted with permission from *In Context*, No.26, Summer 1990: P.O. Box 11470, Bainbridge Island, WA 98110.

"Seikatsu: Japanese Housewives Organize," by Shigeki Maruyama. Reprinted with permission from "The Seikatsu Club": 2-26-17 Miyasaka, Setagaya-Ku, Toikyo 156, Japan.

"Bioregional Economics," by the E.F.Schumacher Society. Reprinted with permission from the *E.F.Schumacher Society Newsletter*, Spring 1985: Box 76, RD 3, Great Barrington, MA 01230.

"Community Supported Agriculture," by Alyssa Lovell. Reprinted with permission from the *Institute for Social Ecology Newsletter*, Spring 1990: P.O. Box 89, Plainfield, VT 05667.

"Amish Economics," by Gene Logsdon. Reprinted from *The New Catalyst*, No. 9, Fall 1987—a shortened version of an article that appeared in *Whole Earth Review*, *Not Man Apart* and *Fourth World Review*.

"Wildwood: A Forest For The Future," by Ruth Loomis and Merv Wilkinson. Extracted and reprinted with permission from *Wildwood: A Forest For The Future*, by Ruth Loomis and Merv Wilkinson, Reflections; 1990, P.O. Box 178, Gabriola Island, B.C. V0R 1X0.

"Living Machines," by David Cayley. Extracted and reprinted with permission from the C.B.C. *Ideas* Series, "The Age of Ecology," Spring 1990, Canadian Broadcasting Corporation., P.O. Box 6440, Station A, Montreal PQ H3C 3L4.

"Free Cities At Work," by David Morris. Reprinted with permission from *Building Economic Alternatives*, Fall 1989: Co-op America, 2100 M Street NW Suite 310, Washington DC 20063.

"Modern Man" cartoons, by bruce von alten are reproduced with permission.*Moderne Man Comics* is available for $9.95 from: O.K. Press, P.O. Box 521, Butte, MT 59703.

MODERNE MAN

MODERNE MAN

b. von alten

1

Green Business In A Gray World — Can It Be Done?

Christopher Plant with David H. Albert

On the island where we live, a group of people committed to disposing of the island's garbage in an ecologically-sound manner recently formed a Recycling Committee. One way or another, they found some land for a recycling depot. Wanting to support their fundraising efforts, I showed up at the site to buy some firewood from them. As I filled the pick-up with wood cut by volunteer labor, I was filled with green angst. For, in order to build the recycling depot, I found they had felled an acreage of forest and bulldozed it clear. I stood on scarred ground amid once magnificent fir and cedar, now reduced to huge piles of dead slash. The irony of the situation struck me as being so typical of the age.

A writer and satirist from a neighboring island who performs a one-man show at "movement" events, frequently has his audiences crying with laughter as he portrays just this kind of irony. He starts one of his pieces with a song, his foot stomping, his face screwed up with anguish as he repeats its one line: "I'm feeling blue, trying to be green...!"

It was a Chinese curse, so the story goes, to live in "interesting times." Nowadays, we might substitute "contradictory" for "interesting," especially if you care about the state of the planet and you're trying to do your responsible bit to keep it from being horribly abused by humankind. For life as an ecologically-aware person *used* to be relatively easy: all you had to do, for a start, was to give up smoking tobacco. Now, however, it's all so very complex. It's not enough to buy tofu and organic vegetables, or try to recycle your garbage and politely refuse those ubiquitous plastic bags at the grocery (and every other) store you happen to frequent. Now, even if you've actually been an environmentalist for a

1

decade or more, you find yourself standing in the supermarket aisles racking your brains over whether you should be buying straight recycled toilet paper, or searching vainly for *non-chlorine bleached* recycled toilet paper, or rejecting the otherwise perfect recycled, non-chlorine bleached toilet paper because it was trucked in from two thousand miles away. Or you may find yourself peering furtively at the fine print on the whole wheat coffee filters, wondering if "natural" means recycled or unbleached or what, at the same time trying to be as inconspicuous as possible because why on Earth are you there buying coffee filters at all (you should be using a recyclable cloth one that tastes awful after a while, shouldn't you?) and, come to think of it, how come you're still even *drinking* the stuff nowadays?? Back home, you pick up your junk mail only to find that maybe as much as half of it is from environmental groups taking their direct mail shots at you. And then you have to try to recall which of them you've decided has integrity any more and deserves your hard-earned money, before reading the newspaper to find that Margaret Thatcher is competing with George Bush as to who is the "greenest" of them all.... These really *are* contradictory times.

They're all the more contradictory, of course, because what we're dealing with is the very essence of the monster. The uncanny "success" of the industrial system is its ability to draw everything into its cold embrace, to reduce all value to dollar values, and to co-opt even its harshest critics. In the late 1960s or early '70s, a huge billboard appeared in the streets of London, England, advertising a well-known beer. It was the epitome of commercial simplicity: giant photographs of Lenin, Mao Tse Tung and Fidel Castro with, beneath, the message, "Revolutionary: Watney's Draft Red Barrel." The power of the system to co-opt the very forces that seek its transformation is no less apparent today with the green fetish. "Green" today is yesterday's red. Both, in their deepest manifestations, represent the same threat to the continuation of business as usual. So both must be co-opted.

There's a wonderful story by a German writer, Michael Ende, called *Momo*. In it, the once carefree population mysteriously begin to lose their *joie de vivre*. Where once there was a happy sense of community among the various tradespeople and shop-keepers, one by one the people seem to change over night. They become anxious, unfriendly, overly money conscious and completely consumed by the idea that they have no time to waste, no time to socialize like they used to, no time at all. It transpires that the town is being taken over by "the men in gray suits" who steal time from people, and it falls to Momo, a young girl, to organize the children and poor people of the town to overcome this insidious influence. Ende's men in gray suits are a wonderful metaphor for western civilization. All fall under their spell. Only those outside the system—the children, the paupers—even have a chance of seeing and avoiding it.

In the context of green business, these stories raise numerous questions. For instance, can green business be the Momo for western industrial society? How can we discriminate between light and deep shades of green business—"light green" indicating a superficial, often profit-dictated, short-term response, while "deep green" might stand for the more authentic attempts at dealing with the profound problem of humankind finding a genuinely sustainable way of inhabiting the planet into the long-term future. *Can* one do green business in a gray world? And what are the limitations and possibilities of green business as a strategy for saving the Earth?

*

In many conversations that we've had with people on these topics, we have been forced to conclude that the very best thing for the planet might be a massive world-wide economic depression. Amid the terrible hardships this would create for countless people, at least the machinery would stop for a while, and the Earth could take a breather. What's significant about this scenario is what it says about the current human occupation of this planet: that it is quite unsustainable, and that business-as-usual cannot be relied upon to steer us off our collision course.

Many would argue that incremental change—gradual greening—*is* succeeding in bringing about positive change and that, moreover, this is the *only* kind of change that is effective. But the examples in Part One of this book suggest otherwise. They show, quite emphatically, that much of what is commonly viewed to be green business is a hoax. The biodegradeable plastic bags are *not* biodegradeable. The recycled paper is likely only *marginally* recycled. And one of the greenest businesses of them all, on the surface—The Body Shop—is, after all, in the cosmetics business, and who needs cosmetics anyway when much of the world's population is hungry and the future of the planet is at stake? In fact, the whole idea that we could possibly do *without* most of these goods is never mentioned, because no one stands to make additional profit from *not* producing things: that alternative lies outside of the market and subsequently receives no attention. In this age of highly sophisticated media manipulation, the public relations *image* that can be portrayed is far more important from a marketing point of view than the actual *content*. To *appear* to be green is the important (and profitable) thing. Summing this up best perhaps is a story from *Utne Reader* about a two-page advertisement that appeared in numerous national U.S. magazines in April 1990, paid for by the 174 members of the Chemical Manufacturers Association. It featured a drawing of Earth and the headline, "HANDLE WITH CARE." Of the nation's 50 worst polluting chemical producers in the U.S.A., 42 percent were sponsors of that ad. Worse perhaps, the environmental movement itself—the original *provocateurs* of green business—have been unable to resist co-option by the giant corporations which are the very worst culprits both environmentally and socially, and which it was the original business of environmental groups to oppose.

On the one hand, green business is like the proverbial motherhood and apple pie: how could one *not* be green, and buy green and contribute to heading us off this collision course? Isn't this what everyone wants? Maybe. But even if everyone did it, green consuming is only a necessary, but not sufficient, step forward. It simply doesn't go far, or deep, enough to make the radical changes needed to reverse the course we're on. And that's because most green business is, in essence superficial. For the production of environmentally friendly goods doesn't address the major structural and institutional obstacles in the way of an authentic greening of industrial society. It doesn't deal with the problem of infinite growth being the mainspring of industry on a finite planet. It doesn't deal with the problem that corporations are legally protected from having to be responsible to people or planet. It doesn't deal with the tremendous consolidation of power by transnational corporations and the governments in their service. It doesn't deal with the ownership of land or the means of production. And it doesn't deal with the enormous social inequities of this world, nor the increasing atomization of society and the commoditization of its cultures.

*

Two related examples may serve to better illustrate the kinds of deep structural change that we might reasonably be expecting of the business world if it were to be genuinely responding to the planetary crisis. One is the role of the state in making the "free" market system work, and the other is the very form by which capitalist business is conducted: the limited liability company.

In the history of North American settlement by Europeans, early visitors to rural pre-Constitution New England noted how production was not organized for an abstract market, but for the production of goods and services specifically needed by neighbors. Community cornhuskings, barn-raisings, log-rolling and quilting bees symbolized the overall cooperation of rural New Englanders. Free credit between local shop-keepers and farmers was assumed, the prosperity of one assuring the prosperity of the other.

The framers of the U.S. Constitution, in contrast, were virtually all representatives of coastal mercantile interests who feared these local communities, with their networks of mutual concern and mutual obligation. For when moral considerations based on traditional and community values came into play, property owners and money lenders were restricted to what the community had to say about how resources were used. Attempts by the emerging state to centralize power and rationalize markets led to two rebellions. The 1787 Shays rebellion in Massachusetts occurred because the state would not heed the will of the majority in maintaining these community-based credit systems, and was specifically directed against the tightening of credit to local communities. And the Whiskey rebellion of 1794 in Pennsylvania was a refusal by western Pennsylvanian farmers to pay taxes on whiskey, for two reasons. First, because whiskey was often used as a local currency, thereby enabling the people to avoid banks and, thus, the payment of interest to bankers; and, second, because the tax was imposed to support a standing army supposedly for the protection of the tax-payers against the Indians, but which was eventually used to put down the Whiskey rebellion.

From its earliest days, then, the "democratic" state in North America could not tolerate diversity in economic values or systems. To make the "free market" system work, the state's role was to eliminate other forms of economic cooperation through the coercive instruments at the state's disposal: sherriffs, police, courts and laws.

The second example is the institution of limited liability offered by the state to corporations and its relationship to the supposed "freedom" of the market. In traditional markets, exchanges of goods occurred between a knowledgeable buyer and seller, with the seller, of course, bearing liability. This reflects a basic principle of democracy: accountability. But in the early days of the U.S., the framers of legal systems thought there might be a need for a limited number of state-chartered corporations where undertakings thought to be in the best interests of the community or state were unlikely to be taken on by single entrepreneurs or limited partnerships operating in a free market. Among the perquisites offered to these corporations (supposedly under the watchful eye of the state), besides "rights of way" or access to state-owned natural resources, perhaps the most important in the long-run was a limit on the liability of those joined in the undertaking. Thus the limited company was created. By treating the corporation as a legal "person," those involved in the enterprise could not be held personally accountable for the effects of their work.

The limited company thus emerged as a special form for specific tasks. But with the increasing pace of western expansion, and the perceived need and market for goods and services, incorporation (and with it, corporate abuse and lack of accountability to any but the stockholders) quickly became the rule, rather than the exception. A business form established for the conditions of "the frontier"—characterized by growth and expansion—is, however, no longer appropriate. For it does not take account of modern conditions which might place higher value on accountability, above all else, as well as the idea of limits to growth, and the interconnection of business with ecology, community and non-material satisfactions.

Pursuing the ecological metaphor, the conditions of the North American settler frontier might be said to approximate those of a "pioneering" ecosystem, whose chief characteristics, according to Edward Goldsmith, are "randomness, individualism, competition, crude external controls and instability." By contrast, the conditions we might like to see today approximate the characteristics of a climax ecosystem: "order, teleology, wholeness, co-operation, stability, and internalized controls" (from Edward Goldsmith, *Gaia: Some Implications for Theoretical Ecology*). Actions of a "deep green" kind might therefore be recognized for their contributing to the evolution of the "climax" phase of human civilization, while shallow, or "light," green initiatives merely serve to perpetuate humankind's pioneering phase.

*

In 1990, then, proclaimed as the year when "democracy and the free market system" (as though they were one and the same) won out over communism, the powers-that-be might be better occupied freeing up our own system instead of bragging about how superior it is to communism. For the "free" market is not accountable, not free and, above all, not democratic. It is not democratic first, because the only values allowed in the marketplace are marketplace values, so those outside the exchange—for example, those with few resources who are therefore not consuming—aren't included and can't compete. In this category also fall nature, future generations and past generations. Second, the state favors those who produce—in fact, the *big* producers—so those who don't produce, as well as the small producers, are at a disadvantage. And, third, democracy assumes the participation of an active, informed citizenry; if the business of information production, editing and dissemination is carried out by the large corporations who also dominate the market, then, by definition, we do not have a democracy. The "free market" is, in short, not appropriate; it is another hoax. But, more than this, it is *the* single most important hoax, from which all others originate. And in the struggle to rescue humankind from grayness, the ultimate objective must be to entirely transform the way we do business together.

With this understanding, contributions to Part One of the book are all of the order "light" green. And we can agree with Sandy Irvine, Barry Commoner and Kirkpatrick Sale that, while green goodies are perhaps welcome, they are also mainly a diversion from the urgent deep structural task ahead. We can hardly hope for societal transformation from recycled toilet paper. In fact, the record shows that if everyone in the United States recycled 100 percent of what now constitutes their personal solid waste, 99 percent of the nation's solid waste would remain. Industry would still be dumping upwards of 4.6 million pounds of toxic chemicals a year into the air, water and soil; the military would still be producing more than 500,000 tons of hazardous wastes a year; plants would still be emitting more than 281 million pounds of known carcinogens into the environment. The solution does not lie with individual consumers changing their individual habits.

We should also emphasise that environmental groups have no business making deals and trade-offs with large corporations, nor accepting their tainted money, if they want to continue receiving our support. Social transformation will not emanate from nefarious enviro-corporate alliances, either.

Furthermore, because the commodity spectacle is so all-engaging, "light" green business tends to merely perpetuate the colonization of the mind, sapping our visions of an alternative and giving the idea that our salvation can be gained through shopping rather than through social struggle and transformation. In this respect, green business at worst is a danger and a trap.

The more authentic strategies for change are those represented in Part Two. From coops that embrace all of life, through community- based currencies and the land trust movement, these examples of the more deep-rooted, bioregional "businesses" attempt to tackle the underlying structure of our relationships with one another and the natural world. For this reason, they give a fuller sense of hope that the idea of greening the way we do things can be a significant force for a more enlightened future. Significantly, they also attempt to embody the two features of pre-Constitution New England that we noted above were systematically attacked by the mercantile class in the late 18th century: the principle of accountability and the obvious benefits of local community solidarity. Equally important, *these* initiatives free up the social imagination to a whole vista of possibilities beyond the stultifying constraints of the conventional marketplace. They take us forward as active participants in a future of our own making and defining, rather than leaving us to be mere consumers at the trough of market-made options.

We need, however, to go much further still, to build upon these examples by stretching the limits of our own imaginings. The Amish, in this collection, give us just the sort of spark to do this, to see beyond the conventional to a completely different way of being. In this global monoculture, such inspiration is not easily found; it must be sought among minority cultures and in histories of the past. Not included in this volume, but nevertheless pertinent are Mohandas Gandhi's Trusteeship Principles: one such source of further inspiration. His overarching ecological principle, for example, may be paraphrased thus: "Nature produces only enough to support our needs from day to day, but never more. When we take more than we need, we are simply either taking from each other, borrowing from the future, or destroying the environment and other species."

His overarching meta-economic principle can be put in the following way, that "Everyone has a right to an honorable livelihood and to have her/his basic needs met, and no more. (Basic needs include: a balanced diet, decent housing, the education of our children in service to the community, reasonable health care and a way to earn the above.)" And from Gandhi's other writings, we can find his primary economic principles as follows:

A. All other wealth above the provision of an honorable livelihood belongs to the community;

B. The community may grant more than that to individuals if it believes that doing so benefits the general welfare.

C. This wealth, however, is a privilege, not a right, and cannot be allowed to contravene the meta-economic principle.

D. There is no "right" of private ownership, except as far as it is permitted by society for its own welfare.

Through this lens, the green consumer products on the supermarket shelves seem far from radical. Gandhi's thoughts jolt us into realizing that saving the world from the men in gray suits is hard, not simple—as Gar Smith's "50 Difficult Things" reminds us, too. In the annals of history, green business is likely to be considered a placebo at a time when far greater change was needed. But, with a continuing effort at pointing out its drawbacks and its failings, it could equally be a seed from which great futures might grow.

Part One

Riding
The Green Bandwagon

MODERNE MAN

2

A Bill Of Goods?
Green Consuming
In Perspective

Debra Lynn Dadd and Andre Carothers

The phenomenon of "green business" has made its most noticeable impact upon the ordinary consumer-in-the-street in the form of a new variety of "green" products available on the supermarket (and other) shelves. As a response to peoples' widely-held and strongly-voiced belief that environmentally-friendly products should be available for the sake of the planet's future, this entry of new items into the consumer arena represents, on the one hand, a welcome breakthrough of ecological consciousness into the world of business.

On the other, less positive, hand, the willingness of business to exploit the green label also epitomizes the very worst and most deceitful characteristics of the so-called free market economy. All too often, instead of genuinely changing business practices, processes and products, the response of corporations has been to cash in on the green bandwagon in a cynical exploitation of the latest market fad. Debra Lynn Dadd, editor of The Earthwise Consumer *and Andre Carothers, editor of* Greenpeace *magazine, examine the business of green consumption and explain why its role in the struggle to save the planet promises to be marginal at best.*

The ad opens with a tableau of children laughing and skipping as they carry green garbage bags across a verdant meadow strewn with litter. As they stuff the trash in bags, a voice-over speaks of the virtues of a clean environment and biodegradable garbage bags. With the field nearly cleaned, a spectral Native American in ceremonial regalia appears, intoning to one awed youngster, "Take what you need, but always leave the land as you found it."

In another commercial, a butterfly flits across the screen, and a pleasant voice patiently details the magnanimity of Chevron, the multi-national oil giant, which has set aside land near one of its refineries to ensure that the rapidly dwindling El Segundo Blue butterfly does not fade into extinction. Who performs such acts of selfless altruism, the viewer is asked? "People Do," responds the oil company.

This is the new environmental advertising, the big-business response to the ecological mood of the public. We'll be seeing a lot more of it in the '90s. The environment, for better or worse (mostly better), is now an "issue." The Michael Peters Group, a design and new products consulting firm, found in a 1989 market research poll that 89 percent of Americans are concerned about the impact on the environment of the products they purchase, more than half say they decline to buy certain products out of concern for the environment, and 78 percent would pay more for a product packaged with recyclable or biodegradable materials.

Environmental concern "is a bigger market than some of the hottest

The Degradable Plastics Scam

A Greenpeace Report

"[Degradable bags] are not the answer to landfill crowding or littering... Degradability is just a marketing tool.... We're talking out of both sides of our mouths when we want to sell bags. I don't think the average customer knows what degradability means. Customers don't care if it solves the solid-waste problem. It makes them feel good."—*Spokesperson for Mobil Chemical Company, manufacturer of Hefty degradable trash bags.*

You are being duped. Most of the products hailed as biodegradable in the marketplace today are little better than their "non- biodegradable" counterparts. Biodegradability means one thing: the material is capable of being broken down by natural processes into pieces small enough to be consumed by micro-organisms in the soil. Plastics, as petrochemical products, are not the outcome of biological evolution, so living things lack the enzymes that can break them down to a molecular level where they can be taken and reincorporated into living things.

So what do these materials do? According to a study commissioned by Greenpeace and conducted by the Center for the Biology of Natural Systems, "biodegradable" plastics can be divided into two categories: those to which starch molecules have been added; and those that have been altered so that they are markets of the '80s," says the journal *American Demographics*. "This is not a small market niche of people who believe in the *Greening of America*," says Ray Goldberg of the Harvard Business School. "It is becoming a major segment of the consuming public." Little wonder, then, that Madison Avenue has turned caring for the environment into a marketing strategy. "The selling of the environment," says Minnesota Attorney General Hubert Humphrey III, "may make the cholesterol craze look like a Sunday school picnic."

"This is not a small market niche of people who believe in the *Greening of America*," says Ray Goldberg of the Harvard Business School. "It is becoming a major segment of the consuming public."

In the case of these two TV ads, the sell is all hype. The first, for Glad

sensitive to light and can at some point break into small pieces. No one has proven that either method breaks down the plastic to the point where it can be metabolized by micro-organisms. But this has not discouraged manufacturers from making false claims about their "environmental friendliness."

The Greenpeace report, *Breaking Down the Degradable Plastics Scam*, analyzed the claims of additive suppliers and plastics manufacturers such as Du Pont, Ecoplastics and Archer Daniels Midland. It determined that none of these major manufacturers could support claims that their products were "biodegradable." The only truly biodegradable plastics are those made from natural polymers such as ICI's PHBV, which is produced by bacteria, and cellophane, which is made of cellulose produced by plants. These products are not in general commercial use because they are currently too expensive or have been replaced by mass-produced plastics. Cellophane has the additional drawback of releasing toxins during manufacture.

Two other concerns stem from these claims of biodegradability. First of all, more than 1,000 additives and colorants, such as cadmium, are used to modify plastics, and these may prove toxic in the environment. The tests for toxicity performed by these companies are inadequate to support their claims of safety, according to the Greenpeace report. And secondly, the role of "biodegradability" in solving the garbage crisis is highly questionable. Reducing and eliminating packaging entirely, rather than tinkering with the contents of the waste stream, is the best solution to the problem.

"biodegradable" garbage bags, fails to mention that truly biodegradable plastic is as rare as the El Segundo Blue. Even if it were available, the pollution released in plastic production puts the Glad Bag's ecological balance sheet squarely in the red. And Chevron is first and foremost an oil company, an industry that is directly and indirectly responsible for much of the pollution on Earth. Back-of-the-envelope calculations suggest that Chevron has probably spent five times as much to boast in magazines and on television of its skimpy list of environmental initiatives than the actions actually cost. (And many of them were required under the provisions of their permits anyway.)

Navigating the misleading claims of opportunistic advertisers is just one of the difficulties facing the consumer intent on "ecologically correct" shopping. So complicated is the terrain, in fact, that what is becoming kown as "green consuming" may prove to be nothing more than a costly diversion from the campaign to save the Earth.

How To Buy Right:

• First, ask yourself if you really need this product, regardless of whether or not it calls itself "environmentally friendly." This should eliminate bleach, fabric softener, drain cleaner, air freshener, everything in aerosol cans, disposable cameras, electric can openers and hundreds of other cleaners, appliances, and plastic trinkets that some copywriter is convinced you couldn't do without.

• Buy the product with the least packaging, and write letters to companies that insist on wrapping everything in layers of plastic and paper.

• Inform yourself, using the dozens of resources available in this book and elsewhere, about boycott targets, non-toxic alternatives, how to make it at home or do without it.

• Elect people to office who will do the right thing—people who are willing to address problems created by the packaging industry, the oil companies, the chemical manufacturers and the investment community.

Blue Angels and Green Seals

The rush to fill the stores of Europe and North America with consumer goods is just one of several leading causes of environmental destruction. The influence of big business has foiled the effort to rein in the consumer culture's worst side effects. One method is to inform consumers of the implications of their purchases, a tradition that inspires consumer rights groups all over the world. Informative labeling is now the method of choice for environmentalists and manufacturers.

The first labeling scheme keyed for ecological concerns was West Germany's Blue Angel program, begun in 1978. The Blue Angel symbol graces over 2,000 products, calling consumers' attention to benefits such as recycled paper and the absence of toxic solvents. Similar schemes are being proposed in nearly every country in Western Europe and now in the United States. They come in three versions: independent, non-governmental efforts, like the United States' new Green Seal program (managed by the Alliance for Social Responsibility in New York); quasi-governmental schemes like those being developed in the United Kingdom and Canada; and identification programs from the manufacturers themselves, like Wal-Mart's new line of "green" products.

Industry's fear of the consumer has produced some notable successes. Before Friends of the Earth in the United Kingdom had launched a planned boycott of CFC-contaminating aerosols, the industry pledged to phase them out. The Blue Angel program can lay claim to preventing 40,000 tons of solvents from entering the waste stream through glossy paints. The concern over agrochemicals in food has given a much-needed boost to the organic food industry, and the boycott of tuna, in conjunction with a federal labeling requirement that may pass the U.S. Congress this year, will play a large role in saving dolphins from the fishing fleet's nets.

But green consuming has its limits. First, seals of approval may be awarded indiscriminately and for the wrong reasons. The Blue Angel, for example, is bestowed on one brand of gasoline-powered lawn mower because it is quieter than a rival. The push variety, soundless and emission-free, gets no award. Loblaws, a Canadian chain of grocery stores, has among its self-proclaimed "green" products a brand of acid-free coffee, so labeled because it does not cause stomach upsets. "Green" batteries are being marketed in the United Kingdom and Canada that contain mercury—considerably less than other brands, but enough to put the lie to claims of environmental friendliness.

Some claims are absurd. "Biodegradable" diapers are filling the developed world's landfills, with no sign that they will ever disappear. West German manufacturer AEG launched a two million dollar ad campaign in England claiming that their dishwashers saved newts. The logic runs like this: since the AEG appliances are slightly more energy efficient, they use less electricity and are therefore responsible for less acid-rain-causing power plant emissions (which, we asssume, kill newts). Arco has launched a "clean" gasoline in California with the slogan, "Let's drive away smog." Both Volkswagen and Audi have touted their cars' low emissions, including "harmless carbon dioxide." If they had done a little homework, they would have discovered that

---

A Field Guide To
The Environmentally Benign Product

(An extremely rare beast. If sighted, purchase immediately.)

• It is not obnoxiously frivolous, like the new electric pepper mill.
• It releases no persistent toxins into the environment during production, use or disposal.
• It is made from recycled material or renewable resources extracted in a way that does not damage the environment.
• It is durable and reusable first, or recyclable or truly biodegradable next.
• It is responsibly and minimally packaged.
• It includes information on manufacturing, such as location, labor practices, animal testing, and the manufacturer's other business.

---

carbon dioxide is a leading greenhouse gas.

The environmental advertising bandwagon offers companies an opportunity to spruce up their images at relatively low cost. Many of the recycled paper products now flooding the market are made by companies with otherwise reprehensible environmental records. In the United Kingdom, according to the company's slogan, "Green means Heinz." But in the Pacific, thanks to tuna fishing, it means dead dolphins. And the term "biodegradable" has been attached to so many different brands of polluting petroleum-based plastics that it has become virtually meaningless, as well as highly misleading.

These companies rely on government regulations for some of their claims, leading to situations like McDonald's declaration that their styrofoam burger trays are CFC-free, when in fact they contain CFC-22, a less potent member of the same chemical family. The lie is based on a glaring example of regulatory sleight of hand: according to the U.S. Environmental Protection Agency, CFC-22 is "technically not a CFC," although for the ozone layer the distinction is far less clear. Under federal law, paper manufacturers can call paper "recycled" when it includes 40 percent recycled content, and that portion consists mostly of paper left over from production processes, not paper that has already been through a consumer's hands and recycled. In Canada, where the Canadian Standards Association creates guidelines for green products, business does its best to ensure that standards are not too stringent. "We make the draft of a guideline," says one insider, "and the industry fights to lower the standard."

All this should raise doubts about industry's claims that they have seen the light, and that hiding behind the advertising pitch is a real concern for the environment that transcends the bottom line. In fact, the record shows that big business is not inclined toward public service. According to a study by Amitai Etzioni of the Harvard Business School, two-thirds of the Fortune 500 companies have been charged with serious crimes, from price-fixing to illegal dumping of hazardous wastes. And these are only the ones that have been caught.

"...the role of green consuming in the fight to save the planet is destined to remain small and marginal."

But even if we could count on the good faith of all concerned, the role of green consuming in the fight to save the planet is destined to remain small and marginal. Consumption's role in destroying the environment is a complex and poorly understood phenomenon. A truly green economy, for example, would require that all products be audited for their effect. Such an audit would analyze the product from "cradle to grave," and include the amount of energy used to produce and transport the item, the pollution generated in its manufacture, the role of the commodity in the economic and social health of the country of origin, the investment plans of the company in question and all its subsidiaries, and the final disposal of the product.

The questions raised by this approach are endless. Does the use of rainforest nuts justify the energy expended transporting them here? Are the labor practices in processing these nuts fair? We all thought the right thing to do was to use paper bags, but if energy use is factored in, some studies show that plastic grocery bags are more environmentally benign (bringing a bag from home doesn't make money for anyone, so you won't see that solution advertised. Should we buy recycled paper from a company known to pollute rivers with pulp mill effluent? Should magazines be printed on chlorine-bleached paper contaminated with dioxin, even if it is recycled and recyclable? Or should they use dioxin-free paper from Europe, even though it is at the moment rarely recycled, and fossil fuels are used to transport it?

Moreover, much of the pollution generated by business is out of reach of the average consumer. For example, as Barry Commoner points out, one of the reasons we have air pollution is that much of the work done by railways has been taken over by trucks, which generate four times as much pollution for each ton hauled. How would the average store owner respond if we demanded only goods that had been delivered by train? And when the beer industry consolidated and discovered that it was cheaper to sell beer in throwaway bottles than in returnables, what possible role could the consumer have played? Between 1959 and 1970, the number of beer bottles produced increased five-fold, while consumption only went up by one-third. Detroit pushes big cars with high-compression, high-pollution engines on the American public not because "that's what we demand," but because that's where the biggest profits are. These decisions aren't illegal, they are simply part of "doing business" in the usual way—a way that puts environmental considerations last.

Finally, individual action, when limited to the supermarket aisles, does little to forward the fundamental changes required to save the Earth. Not only is this collection of individual actions completely outdistanced by the pact of destruction throughout the world, but as Friends of the Earth in the United Kingdom points out, green consuming "leaves totally unanswered the basic questions about global equality and the chronic poverty and suffering of the millions of people in the Third World. ...There is a real danger that green consumerism will divert attention from the real need to change institutional structures." Green consuming labeling schemes, they conclude, "must complement, not become a substitute for, firm government action."

To Consume or Not To Consume: *That* is The Question

Green consuming is still consuming, which is the fundamental paradox. The answer to the problem we face is not only to consume appropriately; it is primarily to consume less. Green labeling schemes are similar in philosophy to the end-of-pipeline pollution control strategies that have failed to stem pollution. They put a dent in the pollution problem, but they do not solve it. The key to protecting the planet is to prevent a problem at the source, rather than tinkering with it after it is already created. In the consumer society, this means intervening early in the game in the decisions about what is produced and how it is produced. A society in which consumption is conscious and restrained requires that new and different decisions be made in corporate boardrooms as well as in national capitals, decisions that put the needs of the planet ahead of the profits of the corporation.

Dolphin-Safe Tuna: Fact or Fish Story?

Roberta Olenick

Consumers concerned about the many dolphins killed annually by the tuna industry should be wary of the increasing number of assurances from canned tuna companies that their products are completely dolphin-safe. Some of these claims are fact, but many are just fish stories.

FACT: The tuna industry catches more than just tuna.

More than 100,000 dolphins die in tuna nets every year—more than 250 every single day! Some populations of these friendly, intelligent marine mammals have been reduced by as much as 80 percent of their original numbers.

Two tuna fisheries are primarily responsible for this irresponsible slaughter—the eastern tropical Pacific (ETP) purse seine fishery for yellowfin, and the high seas driftnet fishery for albacore and other tuna species. In the ETP from southern California down to Chile, where tuna and dolphins school together, fishermen drive both indiscriminately into their encircling nets, using speedboats, helicopters and explosives. Entanglement, suffocation, injury and shock have killed more than six million dolphins in the thirty years since this fishery began. The high seas driftnet fishery claims uncounted thousands of dolphins (and other marine animals) annually in 40-mile long curtains of fine nylon mesh that hang vertically in the water just below the surface, ready to ensnare anything that moves.

FACT: People who love dolphins can still eat canned tuna—if it's in the right can.

Increasing consumer awareness that these fishing practices kill dolphins has created a significant demand for canned tuna products caught by other means. Starkist, the largest producer of canned tuna in the world, was the first to respond to this mounting public pressure for dolphin-safe tuna. On April 12, 1990, the company announced a landmark decision: it would immediately cease all purchase, processing and sale of tuna caught at the expense of dolphins.

To ensure the dolphin-safety of its tuna, Starkist has adopted stringent monitoring procedures. Fish from driftnet vessels are refused outright, and those from ETP purse seiners are accepted only if independent on-board observers from the U.S. government or the Inter-American Tropical Tuna Commission certify that no sets were made on dolphins during the entire trip. This policy applies to all of

Starkist's canneries worldwide, and to all of its tuna-containing products, including pet foods.

One other brand, Chicken of the Sea, now adheres to the "Starkist standard," and is similarly dolphin-safe.

FISH STORY: All dolphin-safe brands of canned tuna are equally dolphin-safe.

FACT: Some are safer than others.

Starkist's revolutionary policy left the rest of the world's tuna industry scrambling to convince consumers that other canned tuna products were also obtained without harming dolphins. In Canada, Admiral, Oceans, Sea Trader, Sea Haul and Pacific Choice are among the ever growing number of brands now advertised as dolphin-safe. Unfortunately, the companies selling these brands each have their own definition of dolphin-safety, none of them as exacting as Starkist's.

Unlike Starkist, these companies do not can their own tuna. Instead they simply put their brand label on cans of tuna imported from processors in Thailand, the Philippines, Malaysia, Japan and other offshore locations. The only "proof" of dolphin-safety they can provide are signed declarations from the presidents of these canneries and other officials with a vested interest in selling tuna. Some of these canneries continue to process driftnetted and other dolphin-*un*-safe tuna, despite claims to the contrary.

FACT: You can help save a drowning dolphin.

1. Restrict your canned tuna purchases to Starkist or Chicken of the Sea, the only two brands that are undeniably dolphin-safe.

2. Urge other canned tuna companies to meet the "Starkist standard." Company addresses are always on the can.

3. Ask the owner or manager of your local grocery store to refuse all in-store dolphin-safe advertisements and product labels from tuna companies whose only "proof" of dolphin-safety is a signed declaration from their supplier.

4. Write your MP or Congressperson, and government ministry of Fisheries. Insist that the government pass legislation prohibiting importation and sale of any tuna caught at the expense of dolphins.

5. Support Earth Island Institute's Save the Dolphins Project, 300 Broadway, Suite 28, San Francisco, California 94133. This environmental group spearheaded the consumer boycott of canned tuna that resulted in Starkist's new dolphin-safe policy.

3

Beyond Green Consumerism

Sandy Irvine

Despite the real pressure that green consuming places on businesses to clean up their acts in order to compete successfully in a more environmentally aware marketplace, and despite the fact that "shopping to save the world" gives people a sense that they can actually do something themselves to tread more lightly on the planet, there are real limits to this kind of movement. The most obvious is that consuming of whatever kind and hue requires money. So it is immediately not a strategy that can be used by those without money: the poor, the disadvantaged, and those of "less-developed" nations. Green consuming is a thoroughly middle class affair. As Sandy Irvine, a Green activist from northern England argues, authentic change toward a conserver society will require, above all, a reduction of the present excessive levels of consumption in the western world.

G reen consumers have realised that in many instances it is possible to change what they consume to the benefit of the environment and of themselves. It is consumer demand that is really putting the pressure on the supermarkets and, in turn, food processors and growers to switch to safer, more sustainable and more humane methods. Green consumers are thereby doing themselves a favor by switching to food that is healthier, tastier and, when all costs are taken into account, often cheaper. At the same time, they are helping to reduce the environmental impact of modern farming.

They can also help reduce world poverty. Products from firms such as Equal Exchange are not only additive-free, but are also bought under fair terms of trade. They can help governments such as that of Nicaragua which, whatever their specific failings, have made unparallelled efforts to promote education and health care as well as more fairly share out land ownership.

Green consumerism puts pressure on government to act. It becomes harder for government to hide behind excuses that there is no demand for change. It bolsters the work of the organized lobbies and pressure groups as well as the greener elements in the major parties. It also rewards those producers and retailers who are making genuine efforts to switch to less wasteful and less polluting alternatives whilst encouraging others to follow suit.

An increasing number of manufacturers are in fact realizing that they can score over their rivals by adapting to environmentalist pressures. One report from Environmental Data Services describes how two battery makers, Varta and Ever Ready, got ahead of their competitors by launching mercury-free products in anticipation of Common Market legislation. Firms slow to catch on often suffer. Both Ford and Austin Rover have lost custom in the car fleet business because they were unable to cope with the demand from customers, such as Great Universal Stores, for unleaded vehicles. Amongst the supermarkets, there has been intense competition as to which is the "greenest of the green."

Most important of all, green consumerism is enabling individuals to act in their own right to help save the world. They do not have to sit back and wait for someone else to take action on their behalf. One individual choosing one brand rather than another may not seem very significant. Yet much environmental destruction is not the product of big projects: it is the consequence of the demand created out of all those little decisions made by each and every one of us every time we go to the shops. For many people, changing what they buy is a practical and realistic first step. They can make a positive contribution, no matter how small, to safeguarding the future.

Moreover, one question often leads to another. When people start questioning how, for example, the food they eat is produced, they are more likely to begin to examine the reality behind all kinds of other products.

The Social and Economic Limits to Green Consumerism

But consumerism equates more possessions with greater happiness. You are what you own, and the more you own, the happier you will be.

Consumerism is seen by some almost as a way of life, not just a matter of popping down to the local shop. Consumerism has created a society in which many people undoubtedly enjoy more physical comforts and ease than their ancestors. But the debit side includes both environmental and social costs.

One of the biggest barriers to green consumerism is the way the economic system makes many wasteful and polluting goods seem alluringly cheap simply because they do not incorporate the full costs of their production or use, passing these costs on to the public and environment at large. Water Authorities, notably in East Anglia, are going to have to pay out large sums of money as a result of agricultural nitrates leaching into rivers. Yet this does not stop the chemical farmers claiming their produce is a lot cheaper than their organic counterparts who, of course, cause no such pollution.

"...saving the environment is going to place limits on what is available in the shops."

The same story repeats itself in the arguments over the cost of free range versus battery produce, of rail versus road transport, of recycled versus virgin paper, etc. Many of the so-called "economies of scale" are only possible because society is picking up the costs of these "externalities" of production. They are also based on very narrow definitions of efficiency, disregarding the resources used, the pollution caused and any impact on the quality of community life.

Freedom of choice is invoked to justify "the voluntary approach" often identified by both government and private enterprise as being preferable to regulation. The concept of the voluntary approach assumes that individuals and organizations have a "right" to abuse the "common" property of soil, water and air on which we all depend. Today's "freedom of choice" often boils down to a refusal to make the choices that really matter. Further erosion of our environmental "life-support systems" will curtail peoples' "freedom of choice" far more dramatically than exercising proper restraint today. The simple truth of the matter is that saving the environment is going to place limits on what is available in the shops. It will mean people saying "no" to certain lifestyles, to certain goods and services, to certain institutions if they are incompatible with what might best be called "a conserver society."

At stake, therefore, in contrast to the traditional goals of consumerism, are certain limitations on the freedom to choose in what are, after all, comparatively trivial areas for the sake of choosing a safe and sustainable way of life for future generations and other species. For our greater well-being we already accept all kinds of restrictions on the right of the individual to do whatever he or she feels like: highway codes, fire regulations, crimes against person and property. There can be no greater crime against posterity than to permit the present slide to environmental disaster to continue.

Equity

There are also fundamental questions concerning equal rights and opportunities that a truly green consumer must face. There is a very real danger, for example, that green consumerism could become something for the well-to-do, while the poorer sections of society have to make do with inferior produce.

Defenders of the free market system claim that a person's willingness to pay is the best way to find out who wants what. This kind of bidding, however, can only take place between people who have the wherewithal to do the bidding! Those with more money, therefore, can command that foodstuffs are grown to feed their pets, not starving human beings. Furthermore, those yet to be born can hardly turn up to make a bid. So if people alive today are prepared to pay lots of money to drive petrol-guzzling cars, there will necessarily be less oil left over for future generations. The market cannot cope with absolute scarcities such as individuals who lack purchasing power or resources that will run out.

At present, even if the "greenest" product is correctly identified and is readily available, its price may be beyond many consumers' means. Many people cannot afford the price of organic produce or of putting a catalytic converter on their car, assuming they own one. Important energy conservation projects, such as insulating your house, still demand a lot of upfront investment even if the cost is paid back over time.

The kind of lifestyle envisaged in *The Green Consumer Guide* would obviously eliminate a great deal of waste and pollution. Nevertheless, if we assume that the green consumer is going to own all the things that the Guide reviews, from "green" dishwashers to anti-perspirants, it is clear that the majority of the world's population will have to do without, and the challenge of global poverty will not be met.

"There is a very real danger, for example, that green consumerism could become something for the well-to-do..."

Genuine green consumerism would boycott those firms who change their products under the pressure of consumer demand or government regulations in one country, but then make no similar changes to what they sell elsewhere. Many companies, especially in the drug and petrochemical industries, have been exposed by organizations such as Oxfam and the Pesticides Action Network for dumping products in the Third World which have been banned in North America and Europe.

However, they would also look beyond such specific abuses and examine the connections between affluent lifestyles and the desperate hardship faced by around one billion people in the "Third World." Poverty has been identified by many organizations and reports as a primary cause of environmental degradation. Poor people are often left, for example, with no choice but to cut down the few surviving trees simply to stay warm and cook what little food they possess. Many people in the Third World can't even get a glass of clean water. Their diets, their housing and every indicator of well-being similarly register a desperate lack of the very basics of life.

This suffering is directly linked to the levels of physical consumption in the richer countries. Americans alone, for example, have used more minerals and fossil fuels during the past half century than all the peoples of the world have used throughout human history. We can only consume strawberries in winter and otherwise defy the seasons by a system of food imports which in effect is starving people in regions such as West Africa. Land that could feed these people is therefore "hijacked" to cater for the demand of the richer lands.

The Ecological Limits to Green Consumerism

Green consumerism is only tackling one part of the equation that determines the level of impact we humans make on our environment—technology. The consequences of the technologies we choose have to be multiplied by two other factors. First there is the sheer number of consumers; then there is the amount each member of a population consumes.

In the next 20 years, there will be nearly two billion more people putting pressure on an already depleted planet. Furthermore, rising human numbers are being accompanied by rising expectations of goods and services as the luxuries of yesterday become the "necessities" of today.

The vital point here is that the crisis has come about not from any one of these pressures, but because of the effect they have in multiplying each other. It is as foolish to blame everything on overpopulation as it is to leave it out of the equation.

Population growth is the factor that by itself worsens all other social and environmental problems, whatever their immediate cause. Having no more than two children is the most effective action a couple can take. Yet not one green consumer guide even mentions the importance of individual responsibility in this matter. Indeed, *The Green Consumer Guide*, subtitled "From Shampoo to Champagne," is quite careful to give the impression that we are not being asked to give up too much.

The size of the human population and the power of its technology are now such that we are creating environmental damage on an immense scale. We create it not only by specific pollutants (what we put into the environment), but also by ecological degradation as we erode its richness and variety.

Part of the problem of pollution today is its sheer volume. Natural systems can break down and recycle biodegradable wastes as long as we keep them within limits of tolerance. However, overpopulation and overconsumption are swamping nature's ability to do so. The problem of quantity has been compounded by that of quality, by the revolution in the kinds of materials we have created—from plastics to plutonium—which nature is unable to break down and recycle. Most dangerous is the disturbance of the planet's heat balance caused by human activity, particularly from the burning of fossil fuels and wood.

"The Green Consumer Guide, **subtitled "From Shampoo To Champagne," is quite careful to give the impression that we are not being asked to give up too much."**

There are real limitations to various economic and technological "fixes" that are being proposed, including green consumerism. At best, they buy time; often they only swap one problem for another.

One economic measure that is increasingly being discussed is the "polluter pays" principle. It is argued that the best way to tackle anti-social and anti-environmental actions is to make the guilty parties pay for the costs of the damage they cause.

Though this approach appeals to natural justice, there are problems to be resolved. Many forms of pollution are a combination of substances from many diverse sources. It is difficult to calculate fairly who should pay what costs.

Some consequences of pollution are irrevocable, so that no amount of taxation can make amends, even if we could put a price on what has been lost. It is also fundamentally unjust to allow someone to continue to destroy the environment simply because they are prepared to "pay for the privilege."

Lurking beneath such proposals is the false idea that there is such a thing as "optimal pollution." In fact, we simply do not know in advance the safe levels of toxic substances or what ecosystems can tolerate over time. Usually, when some conclusive evidence does come to light, we have belatedly had to revise our estimates downwards (e.g. "optimal" levels of radioactive pollution). In any case, it is simply wrong to trade away fundamental rights (e.g. of children at risk from car pollution or a species threatened with extinction by habitat destruction) just because the monetary calculations of costs and benefits make it seem financially profitable.

Moreover, most pollution is not the product of a failure to make use of waste byproducts which, with a few more incentives, could be turned into new forms of wealth or replaced by substitutions. Rather, they are the inevitable consequence of increased production and increased consumption. For this reason, the approach focusses on the wrong end of the production system—its outputs—rather than the all-important initial input of energy and raw materials.

In sum, therefore, pollution charges can be useful as a "fine-tuning" instrument that discourages some specific products and processes. But it cannot cope with the general crisis of resource depletion, pollution and environmental degradation we now face.

The other main technological "fix" are "bolt-on" devices to curb pollution. But the potential of pollution gadgetry and technological substitution is sometimes exaggerated by looking at only one part of the overall picture of environmental impact. Complete thermodynamic and ecological bills are not being fully kept in the accounts of Green Consumerism, as is spotlighted by the nonsensical description by both the Elkington/Hailes and Seymour/Girardet books of electric cars as non-polluting. What about the resources consumed and pollution caused by electricity generation? The energy and raw materials to make the car and the batteries? Will they not need roads, traffic lights, garages?

We should, of course, be making use of the best available technologies but they cannot help evade the challenge of reducing the sheer volume of traffic of goods and people.

Building Political Constituencies

Green consumerism is a great step forward and has great potential. Yet it must not be allowed to reinforce complacency by suggesting that all we need to do is make a comparatively small number of changes and then all will be well. Nor should it divert attention from the need to change the institutional and regulatory framework of society by a one-sided focus on the individual. Its biggest failing is to be found in the idea that environmental problems are due to the kind of produce we are consuming.

The truth of the matter is that humanity as a whole is going to have to consume not just better but less. The solution to pollution is simply to generate less pollution in the first place. The only way to halt and reverse environmental degradation is less building over open spaces and less intensive land usage.

Genuinely green consumerism, therefore, would focus on reducing rather than simply changing personal levels of consumption. This would work against society's economic structures and many other social institutions which are based on the "more is better" mentality. It would also make central the notion of equity between social groups, between countries, between generations and between species. It would pay attention not just to our material needs but also to the spiritual side of our being.

Hopefully, however, green consumerism will stimulate an increasing number of people to examine critically both their own lifestyles and society as a whole. A truly green consumer would be asking first and foremost "do I really need all these things?" It would involve a change to thinking in terms of what is the minimum necessary to satisfy essential human needs, rather than novelty, fashion, status and all the other hooks of materialism.

"Genuinely green consumerism, therefore, would focus on reducing rather than simply changing personal levels of consumption."

Action must in fact be planned at four levels: global; national; local; personal. There is no one answer to the crisis. Its solution depends upon a judicious combination of many means—taxation, financial incentive and penalties, direct regulations, education, and personal lifestyle change. In a review of the sales of phosphate-free detergents, one report noted that their share of the Swiss market was 100 percent. The reason is simple. The Swiss Government has simply banned phosphate-containing detergents to save their lakes from eutrophication. Providing that such measures are put to the electorate, this is a simpler, fairer and more democratic way of saving the environment. The time factor is vitally important. How much more damage will be done if we wait for the slow percolation of green consumerism to drive such products off the supermarket shelves, rather than take decisive action today?

Though few people can have illusions about the huge amount of work to be done in mobilizing public opinion to support a concerted program of government action, it is here that the fate of the environment will ultimately be decided, not in what individuals do at the shopping counter. The two initiatives must still go hand in hand. Green consumerism itself could become a far more powerful weapon as a campaigning tool, with individuals joining others to persuade their fellow citizens to boycott certain damaging produce, to support manufacturers and retailers who are making genuine efforts, to lobby local and national government to ensure that their purchasing programs and other operations reflect green criteria.

What is appropriate will vary from one person to the next, but joining forces with other people is an essential part of the process. It is here that campaigning work can be organized to persuade the unconverted. It is here that ideas can be pooled and detailed policy alternatives worked out. It is here that people can support and sustain each other's commitment to protecting our planet.

In parallel with green consumerism, there must therefore be concerted action to build the political constituencies to implement sustainable policies. Without such political change, green consumerism will merely postpone the day of reckoning.

Surviving The "Green Nineties:" Becoming A Ccrporation With An Environmental Conscience

A Conference prospectus from the Institute for International Research, New York

THE GREEN CONSUMER REVOLUTION

Chicago, IL. November 13 & 14th, 1990.

Dear Executive,

The South American Rain Forest. The Ozone Layer. The Alaskan oil spill. The environment is at the forefront of today's news and it is uppermost in the minds of today's consumers. Increasingly, consumers are basing their buying decisions on two things: whether or not a product is more environmentally sound than another, and on the image of the company who produced that product.

Today's consumer is tying buying decisions to the environmental image of the product, the manufacturing process used to create that product, and the corporate stance on environmental issues. In other words, the environment is increasingly impacting your bottom line, and needs to play a key role in both current and future marketing strategy.

This conference is designed for you, the marketing and public relations professional. It will show you not just how to "jump on the environmental bandwagon," but how to implement change throughout the whole process, including corporate philosophy and future planning, and how to publicize the real changes and positive environmental planning that your company is undertaking.

Responding to consumer demands and interests often starts at the marketing and public relations levels. As marketing and public relations professionals, you are often the first to hear directly from consumers what their wants, fears and needs are. Find out how to let your customers know that you are listening to them and taking action towards helping to prevent lasting environmental problems.

As marketers you are in a position to effect change. Consumers want the companies that they buy products from to be more environmentally sensitive. **By identifying these consumers and their buying power, you can actually help make your company more environmentally fit, enhance your corporate image and increase profits.**

BEING AS ENVIRONMENTALLY SOUND AS POSSIBLE MAKES GOOD BUSINESS SENSE

Practically all companies will find in the near future that environmental responsibility will have an increasingly important role to play in their overall corporate image. It is generally recognized that companies which are perceived to operate in a socially and morally "responsible" manner enjoy a better reputation which directly influences sales figures and the ability to attract and retain customers.

The rapidly increasing interest in ecological issues has focused attention on companies' environmental attitudes and many companies have already begun to change elements of their behavior to meet this new concern. You can't afford to lag behind your competitors!

Hear case studies and detailed representations from companies who are attempting to become more environmentally sound and market themselves and their products as such.

...The conference, through lectures and case studies, will teach you how to build a better environmental corporate identity—in practice—from leading marketing and environmental experts. The conference will focus on reaching the environmentally concerned consumer, enhancing corporate image and building a sound environmental profile. You'll also have much-needed networking time to swap ideas with colleagues who are facing the same challenges you are.

MORE THAN A TREND, BEING ENVIRONMENTALLY SOUND IS GOOD FOR YOUR BUSINESS

By doing all that you can for the environment, your coporate philosophy of being concerned, caring and committed translates into goodwill and loyalty for your products and for your company. Being environmentally sound is good for business and good for everyone.

...I look forward to greeting you this November in Chicago.

> Sincerely,
> Sheryl Frankel, Vice President

P.S. 77% of American consumers say their purchase decisions are affected by a company's reputation on environmental issues. This is a market you can't afford to ignore!

P.P.S. Here is just a sampling of the companies represented at our past "Green Consumer" conferences: Coca-Cola Foods, Eastman Kodak Company, Lever Brothers, S.C. Johnson Wax, Colgate Palmolive, Cheserought-Ponds, Duracell, Procter & Gamble, Turner Broadcasting Systems, Weyerhaeuser, Scott Paper, Ecological Society Project, Rain Forest Alliance, Fidelity Investments, IBM, Ciba Geigy, Airwick, Conservation International, The Dial Corporation, Thrifty, Hallmark Cards, and many more....

4

The Greening Of
International Finance

Brian Tokar

Many of the worst offenders of the corporate world are multinational companies which operate globally, beyond the laws of mere nation states, and with no loyalty to place anywhere on the planet. Seeking cheap labor and lax environmental regulations, these behemoths of the business world frequently establish themselves in the poor nations of the Third World. Aided—if not pushed—by First World governments, the "less-developed" nations are now in debt (mostly for things they never needed) to western banks and governments to the tune of billions of dollars. The poor people of these nations were not the ones who took on this debt, nor were they the ones to benefit from it, and they never took part in the decisions to go into debt. The debt belongs, properly speaking, to the capitalist bankers of the Third and First Worlds who assumed it on an undemocratic basis.

Enter, stage right, "corporate environmentalism" brandishing the solution of "debt-for-nature swaps:" an apparently green approach to both rainforest depletion and Third World debt which, at best, simply buys some time for the rainforests. But doesn't it stretch credulity to the limits to imagine just how the halls of the international finance establishment—the epitome, perhaps, of the problem, of dark gray business—could possibly be "greened?" Brian Tokar, a writer and activist from Vermont, investigates.

Few international environmental issues in recent years have raised as much widespread concern or as much passion as the fate of the world's tropical forests. Tropical forests are the Earth's greatest reservoir of biological diversity, housing up to three quarters of all living species. They hold massive amounts of organic carbon and release globally-significant quantities of oxygen. Their human inhabitants include many of the last remaining tribal peoples whose traditional ways have not been compromised by the intrusion of civilization. The crippling indebtedness of many tropical nations, especially Brazil, has brought pressure for a wave of new development schemes, in which vast tracts of rainforest are being destroyed to satisfy the demands of international banks. Rainforest activists predict that if the destruction continues at present rates, there will be no tropical forests left in just 20 or 30 years.

In the 1980s, several Third World countries began to resist continuing debt payments. Citing the effects of foreign debt on their national economies and the fact that many loans have already been paid several times over in exorbitant interest payments, several countries have threatened to default on their loans. Others have slowed debt payments to a trickle, forcing banks to admit that many Third World loans will simply never be repaid.

Anxious to keep these countries "in the system," the banks continue to loan countries money to support debt payments, while proposing new, more destructive development projects and imposing ever-stricter austerity measures. In an effort to squeeze some tangible benefit from these increasingly dubious loans, banks have become increasingly involved in international debt-swapping. They are directly trading portions of various countries' debt for equity in debtor countries, stakes in future development and, most significantly for environmentalists, commitments for the preservation and "sustainable management" of parcels of tropical forest land. Organizations like the World Wildlife Fund, Conservation International, and the Nature Conservancy are actively sponsoring so-called "debt-for-nature swaps," promoting them as vehicles for "The Greening of International Finance."

"Debt-for-nature swaps, like the equity swaps upon which they are modeled, raise serious questions about both local and national sovereignty."

The first, and by far the best publicized, of these "swaps" was launched in 1987 when the Frank Weeden Foundation of Connecticut granted $100,000 to Conservation International (CI) for the purchase of $650,000 in unpaid debt from Citibank affiliate in Bolivia. In exchange, the Bolivian government agreed to support the expansion of the Beni Biological Reserve, an ecologically unique area containing some of the world's largest remaining reserves of mahogany and tropical cedar. The

Reserve itself would become protected "to the maximum extent possible under Bolivian law," according to CI, and would be surrounded by a much larger "multiple use and conservation" buffer zone, for a total of almost four million acres. The Bolivian government agreed to allocate $250,000 (mostly from funds generated through US-sponsored food aid) toward the management of the project. CI would provide training, technical support and other forms of international assistance for the project, and advise local agencies on the "sustainable use" of the precious mahogany forests.

Supporters of the project assert that the entire area might have been stripped of trees before the next century had Conservation International not intervened, while critics argue that the entire project is merely a vehicle for the more rational exploitation of the area. Some accounts report that logging in the buffer zone has increased tremendously since the project began: twice as many mahogany trees were removed in 1988 as in 1987, for example. Contracts for seven new sawmills in the area were approved immediately before the debt swap went into effect. Residents of the area were not consulted before the debt-swap agreement was signed, even though much of the land was already in dispute between logging companies and the area's 5,000 native inhabitants.

Experts in so-called "sustainable development"—one of the key catchphrases of corporate environmentalism—have carved the land up into experimental parcels which will experience varying degrees of tree harvesting, from the most limited to the most intensive. For the native people, these are trees that would have been used to build homes and canoes, and to shelter local wildlife for countless generations to come. The Moxeno and Chimane people have seen environmentalists thwart their efforts to manage the land as a community—the project's needs were apparently better served by continuing the Bolivian government's practice of maintaining native lands in isolated private plots, the preferred model in much of Latin America.

Debt-for-nature swaps, like the equity swaps upon which they are modeled, raise serious questions about both local and national sovereignty. The land ostensibly remains under the host country's control, but patterns of use are determined by international organizations. More recent programs in Ecuador, Costa Rica, Madagascar and other countries set aside funds from the national government for conservation bonds and general land "improvement" programs instead of designating specific tracts of land. Still, these efforts reinforce international (read corporate) control over the debtor countries' development and budgetary priorities, while giving the banks an opportunity to make good on essentially bad loans. Beside the public relations value of donating small portions of their debt portfolio to environmental causes, the banks often gain significant tax breaks, as both the loss in loan value and the value of the donation for the sponsoring environmental group are tax-deductible. CI is lobbying Congress to make the full book value of donated debt tax deductible. In some cases, banks have donated hundreds of thousands of dollars in Third World debt directly to groups like CI and the Nature Conservancy. Of course, most of the countries involved remain indebted to international banks to the tune of many billions of dollars.

"Without native protection, wildlife habitats might be designated for preservation today, but can be eliminated tomorrow at the stroke of a pen or the roll of a bulldozer."

Concerns about the impact of such schemes have arisen in Africa, where several countries are discussing plans for future debt-for-nature arrangements. Africans have already had some difficult experiences with North American conservationists. In 1909 Teddy Roosevelt went there and reportedly shot a third of the rhinos in Uganda. Groups like the World Wildlife Fund, with encouragement from wealthy big game hunters and safari enthusiasts, have been involved in the creation of National Parks in several African countries. The parks, conceived on the American model, are seen as pristine places where wild animal habitats can be preserved without human disturbance. This often happens at the expense of native peoples, who have been living alongside wild animals for countless generations and, in many cases, fought to keep slave traders, poachers and colonialists out of these areas. Without native protection, wildlife habitats might be designated for preservation today, but can be eliminated tomorrow at the stroke of a pen or the roll of a bulldozer. The damage could be done before international wildlife groups knew what was happening.

In Kenya and Tanzania, the pastoral Masaai people have protected elephants and other animals from hunters since the beginnings of European colonialism, but are being systematically excluded from National Parks planned with support from U.S. environmentalists. Moringe Parkipuny, a Masaai elder who represents his people in the national parliament of Tanzania, explains: "To us in Africa, the disappearance of the elephant is just one aspect of the major problem of colonialism.... The conflict, as we see it, is between indigenous peoples and the policies imposed on them by foreign governments. These policies discriminate against us by making wild animals more important than indigenous peoples. They have also turned our people against wild animals, because they feel that wildlife is now being used as a weapon to destroy us."

By blinding themselves to underlying political factors, U.S.-based

---

The New Environmental Funds: Cashing In Or Cleaning Up?

Susan Meeker-Lowry

Concern for the environment reached an all time high in 1990. According to a *New York Times* poll taken in July, 80 percent of the American people agreed with the following statement: "Protecting the environment is so important that the requirements and standards cannot be too high, and continuing environmental improvements must be made *regardless of cost*" (my emphasis). In the grand old American tradition of capitalizing on a good thing, a number of so-called environmental funds are cropping up. Merrill Lynch initiated their Environmental Technology Trust, a five-year fund designed to perform like a traded stock. Fidelity Investments initiated an environmental fund which is part of their Select Portfolios group that invests in different industry sectors. The SFT Environmental Awareness Fund (EAF) is another newcomer that started as a generic growth fund transformed into its current environmental focus in December 1988.

There is no question that these funds exist first and foremost to make money. SFT Family of Funds' President Wes Groshans agrees: "This is a solid industry, regardless of what the social values might be. The industry is a tremendous economic opportunity at this time." Rosemary Mills-Russell, VP of Merrill Lynch also notes, "It's difficult to say whether the interest is more altruistic or opportunistic."

Exactly what "industry" are they referring to? For the most part, these funds invest in firms specializing in toxic and hazardous waste clean-up, air and water pollution control and clean-up, as well as incineration plants. A new bi-weekly magazine, *Hazardous Waste Business*, published by McGraw-Hill ($495/year) is self-described as "the leading publication covering hazwaste...approaching the industry as a business...that is already drawing two billion dollars a year in public and private investments, and is expected to exceed $200 billion over the next 50 years." Major polluters, including AMOCO Oil and Texas Instruments are getting in on the action, creating treatments and facilities (including incineration) for their hazardous wastes. The industry also includes newer companies dealing exclusively with what is euphemistically called "waste management."

environmental organizations become unwitting agents of imperialism overseas, just as they sometimes help to rationalize polluting practices at home.

EAF's list of companies includes the notorious Waste Management Inc. (one of the world's largest disposers of waste, known for its ecologically catastrophic practices) and Browning Ferris as well as builders of mass-burn incinerators like Ogden. Their portfolio includes a builder of nuclear power plants (Combustion Engineering) and their prospectus states that the fund is allowed "to invest partially or completely in defensive securities including U.S. Government securities." These companies are not out to heal the Earth—they are set up to cash in on the booming waste industry. These companies, whether they are large or small, *directly benefit* from the production of wastes—so do their investors. The more waste we generate—of any kind, in any place—the more profit these companies make. We should be channeling our investment dollars into ways of minimizing the production of wastes at the source, rather than on ways of dealing with it after the fact. We must become aware of waste as a valuable resource and treat it as such. There are many organizations doing just this. Think of it—if we are successful in reducing waste at the source we will put many of the companies currently profiting from the hazwaste (and other waste management) industry out of business. Larry Martin, a consultant on waste issues, notes that the billions "spent annually on hazardous waste management, and all other pollution control costs, actually contributes to the GNP." He feels it is a conflict of interest to have this industry contributing to our so-called indicator of economic prosperity and favors the term "Gross National Waste Product" as the true indicator of our situation.

What is the environmentally concerned investor to make of all this? I would encourage anyone thinking about investing in these new environmental funds to request a copy of their investments. You probably won't have heard of most of the companies, however there will be some (like Waste Management Inc.) that will stick out. Obtain the addresses of the unfamiliar companies (either from the funds themselves or in the library) and write for a copy of their annual report which will tell you exactly what kind of business they engage in. If you agree that these new funds are "iffy" at best, support instead such progressive and positively focussed funds as the New Alternatives Fund (516-466-0808) which invests in alternative and renewable sources of energy production while avoiding polluters and defense contractors. This fund has been around since 1982 and has an impressive track record. Other screened funds, including Calvert, Parnassus and Pax World, have environmental screens that may not be the strictest (depending on your perspective) but you probably will not be profiting from increased production of toxics.

5

Endorsing Green Capitalism: Should Environmental Groups Get Into Bed With Business?

Wayne Ellwood

The ability of large corporations to wield their enormous power to co-opt the forces that oppose them is well-known. But their success in using the green bandwagon to seriously divide the environmental movement has been shocking. Yet, driven by the free-market imperatives of this era, environmental groups— especially the bigger, more established among them—have seen green consumerism as a means of making a buck for their coffers, too. This has meant making some unlikely bed partners, to say nothing of some disillusioned environmental supporters. As a consequence, it has also raised to broader consciousness the whole question of the proper role and ethics of environmental groups: whether they should sell products at all, and how much they should accept funding from business. Co-editor of The New Internationalist, *Wayne Ellwood, investigates one of Canada's green business scandals.*

The news swept through the Canadian environmental movement last year like a toxic blast: Pollution Probe, Canada's oldest and best-known environmental group, had publicly endorsed a line of "green" products created by the country's largest supermarket chain, Loblaws. In return for giving Loblaws its official seal of approval, Probe was to receive a royalty on sales.

Worse still: Probe's erudite and respected Executive Director, Colin Isaacs, had also agreed to play environmental salesperson for Loblaws. Canadians long used to seeing environmental campaigners arguing with corporate polluters were stunned to turn on their TV sets and see Isaacs rubbing shoulders with Loblaws' gnome-like marketing genius, David Nichols. Surrounded by a small mountain of "green" diapers—made with non-chlorine bleached paper and photo-sensitive plastic—Isaacs told viewers, "If you must use disposable diapers, then use this one."

The union of environmentalist and marketing executive was both innovative and shocking. Within Pollution Probe five staffers resigned in protest and Isaacs quit soon after, citing lack of board support for his position. Probe's liaison with the giant grocery chain—Loblaws has 30 percent of Canadian supermarket sales—sparked an instant debate among environmentalists about what kind of relationship they should have with business.

The Pollution Probe staff quit for several reasons. Gord Perks, then in charge of waste management at Probe, claims, "Staff were not consulted. The decision to endorse Loblaws' "green" products was made by Isaacs and a few board members. Even today a small group makes most of the decisions."

Many staff were embarrassed by the way the decision had been taken. "I literally found out about our endorsement of used motor-oil from someone I was phoning to find out whether the stuff was OK," says the group's Education Program Co-ordinator at the time, Dave Bruer. "When we asked to see test results so we could recommend the products with some confidence we were told that the data was confidential, between Colin Isaacs and Loblaws." Probe's Information Officer at the time, Vanessa Alexander, felt completely compromised by the Loblaws' deal. "In my view disposable products are not green," she says. "I could not in good conscience tell people to buy disposable diapers."

"Pollution Probe was to receive a royalty on sales—up to $75,000 maximum during the first year of the agreement."

Staff also felt great unease about a major environment group cozying up to big business; a significant minority of Probe's employees at the time were opposed to promoting products from any corporation. "Credibility is the environment movement's most important asset," explains activist and lawyer Steven Shrybman of the Canadian Environmental Law Association (CELA). "Our opinion isn't worth anything if people think it is influenced by self-interest."

From Loblaws' point of view the deal was a bargain. The company was able to display Probe's endorsement prominently in advertising and on the products themselves. In return, Pollution Probe was to receive a royalty on sales—up to $75,000 maximum during the first year of the agreement. The company actually sold five million dollars worth of "green" products in Ontario alone during the first month. Today Loblaws makes about half a million dollars a week on its 20 or so "green" products—and sales are increasing.

The company's spokesman, Paddy Carson—a verbose Irishman with an impressive lay command of environmental issues—says that since the row over Probe's involvement, Loblaws has been deluged with letters of support. "The criticism didn't do anything but boost sales," he admits.

The key player in Probe's decision to promote "green" products is Colin Isaacs. He saw the Loblaws link as a chance to use "consumer power" to make quick progress on environmental issues. Like most activists, Isaacs is fed up with the sloth-like pace with which governments are taking on environmental concerns. "After a while you feel you're banging your head against a brick wall," he says. "The problems are tremendous and time is short; we can't afford to wait while politicians figure out what to do."

According to Isaacs the endorsement strategy has already begun to pay off. He cites the proliferation of non-chlorine bleached paper products as a good example. Both environmentalists and public health groups have long been worried about toxic discharges from paper mills using chlorine bleach.

Environmental groups have been lobbying for years about the issue. But neither government nor industry have shown much interest. Now consumer pressure is forcing pulp and paper companies in Western Canada to think about reducing or eliminating the chlorine bleach part of the pulp process. Brisk sales of Loblaws' non-chlorine bleach diapers and sanitary napkins have proven that eco-sensitive consumers will switch their buying habits in favor of the environment.

Even Isaacs' harshest critics agree with his basic analysis: public concern over the environment should be used to put pressure on manufacturers through the marketplace.

But the real danger is that "buying green" will be seen as the ultimate solution to the environmental crisis. Consumers, finally satisfied that they can "do something," may seek no further than their shopping trolleys to help the planet.

But "green products" on their own don't really touch the heart of the problem: at issue is the ideology of consumerism that pervades party politics of left, right and center. "It's over-consumption that got us into this mess in the first place," says Julia Langer, Director of Friends of the Earth, Canada.

Over-consumption is a key concern for Colin Isaacs too. But he argues that Canadians have one of the most consumer-oriented societies on Earth. "We know we have to reduce consumption but we're going to get change more quickly if we do it step-by- step. We're a nation of shoppers so let's use that shopping habit to achieve something right now."

Greening The Board Rooms?

Eric Mann

In the wake of the Exxon Valdez incident, which was in the wake of Bhopal, Three Mile Island, Love Canal, and more..., there is a growing movement within the corporate world for each board of directors to appoint a token "environmentalist." So far, no one from the Citizens Clearinghouse for Hazardous Wastes has been contacted—nor would I hope that they would be active if drafted. Instead, the preferred "environmentalists," according to the *L.A. Times*, must be people sensitive to the corporate profitability objectives. Not surprisingly, the omnipresent William Ruckelshaus was recruited to the board of the chemical giant Monsanto; William K. Reilly, Environmental Protection Agency chief and then president of the Conservation Foundation, was brought on to the board of Northeast Utilities, and Alice Rivlin, chairman of the governing council of the Wilderness Society, makes substantial fees for serving on the board of Union Carbide, whose negligence was responsible for thousands of deaths at Bhopal.

The danger of "greening the boardroom" is that since boards of directors are specifically charged with maximizing profitability of corporations and the types of "environmentalists" chosen will fully endorse the corporate agenda, what will in fact be constructed is a new layer of corporate apologists attacking grassroots environmental movements—just as former United Agricultural Workers president Douglas Fraser was brought on to the board of Chrysler not to restrict corporate behavior but to rubber-stamp the 57,000 permanent layoffs and 11 plant closings Lee Iacocca was about to implement.

So the institutional matrix is frightening—corporate polluters derailing environmental regulations in Congress, corporate pollution managers making lucrative deals that neither restrict the polluters nor clean up the toxics, government agencies set up to protect the environment becoming captive to the polluters and pollution managers, and the corporate boards of polluters co-opting the most malleable and greedy "environmentalists" to clean up their own image—but not their products. In this context, talk about "grassroots organizing" must go beyond a romantic perspective to an analytical and long term strategic perspective that challenges institutional power as a means to establish democratic policy.

6

Marketing The Environment

Brian Tokar

*In the decade when everyone wants to be an environmentalist, the environ-
ment itself has become big business. In turn, this has led to environmental
organizations changing their style and structure to become more acceptable to
a mass public as well as to potential donors from the newly converted corporate
sector. The result, in the U.S., has been a steady evolution of certain environmental organizations towards "the system" and the emergence of "official"
environmentalism, complete with Washington, D.C. offices, multi-million dollar budgets, and slots within the established corridors of power. As Vermont
activist and writer, Brian Tokar, explains, this metamorphosis is not necessarily
of benefit to the planet. On the contrary, the rules of the game—cooperation and
compromise—seem to have led to wheeling and dealing "pollution credits,"
deliberate misinterpretation of the record of environmental defence to date, and an
unwillingness to squarely face the real problem: that of economic growth, the
engine of the industrial juggernaut.*

Every major opinion poll of recent years shows a growing popular
concern with the ecological crisis. Increasing numbers of people—
up to 70 percent in some surveys—acknowledge a conflict between
environmental protection and economic growth and choose in favor of
the environment. Radical ecologists, from the Greens to Earth First!,
strike an increasingly responsive chord with statements about the roots
of ecological devastation in our economic system and our way of life.
The powers that be are clearly worried, and will do everything they can
to moderate and soften the widespread renewal of popular ecological
activism before it is truly out of control.

The field of discourse within the environmental movement has become increasingly polarized in recent years. But while discussions on
the Left focus upon more radical developments and the various conficts

among them, established national environmental organizations, almost all now based in Washington, D.C., have been moving steadily in the direction of accommodation to the system. In the past year, many commentators have proclaimed a so-called "third wave" of environmentalism, which differs from both the conservation of the early 1900s and the activism of the 1960s and 1970s in its open advocacy of market-oriented measures for addressing environmental tradeoffs and "offsets" negotiated with corporate polluters and, in an ultimate stroke of arrogance and opportunism, plans for an open market in tradeable "rights" to pollute.

This openly pro-corporate form of environmentalism represents a logical next step in the continuing sellout of official environmentalism. Throughout the 1970s and 1980s, environmentalists have become an increasingly visible and increasingly entrenched part of the Washington scene. As the appearance of success within the system grew, organizations began to restructure themselves and alter their personnel so as to enhance their ability to play the game. The environmental movement became a stepping stone in the careers of a new generation of Washington lawyers, and official environmentalism increasingly accepted the role long established for other public regulatory advocates: that of helping to assure the smooth functioning of the system.

"...established national environmental organizations, almost all now based in Washington, D.C., have been moving steadily in the direction of accommodation to the system."

These changes became entrenched with the right-wing shift in Washington politics and Washington political culture during the Reagan years. With access to vast new funds, often gained through appeals to people's outrage against Reagan's anti-environmentalism, the major environmental organizations assumed an increasingly top-down, corporate-style structure. Internal battles in organizations like the Sierra Club, Friends of the Earth, and Greenpeace were invariably won by those advocating a more corporate style and attitude, and avoidance of issues and tactics that might prove alienating to wealthy donors. Prominent activists like David Brower, once the "archdruid" (in John McPhee's famous *Encounters*) of the Sierra Club and Friends of the Earth, and Dave Foreman, Wilderness Society lobbyist turned Earth First! founder, expressed their dismay with this trend and were squeezed out of leadership roles in the major national organizations.

The Rise of Corporate Environmentalism

Official environmentalism grew tremendously in the 1980s. The Sierra Club grew from 80,000 to 500,000 members, and the conservative National Wildlife Federation reported membership gains of up to 8,000 a month. The World Wildlife Fund, with its dubious record in many Third World countries, grew almost tenfold, while the Natural Resources Defense Council (best known for its anti-pesticide work) has doubled its membership since 1985. Many groups became masters of direct mail, using each new environmental disaster to gain members for their organization, whether the organization was actively working on the issue or not. The oil spill in Alaska's Prince William Sound was a classic example: there was a resounding expression of outrage in the form of newspaper ads and press conferences, but no genuinely forceful response from environmentalists and no substantively new proposals. Everyone demanded a "proper" cleanup, along with protection for the Wildlife Refuge in the far north of Alaska, but no nationally recognized organization called for the closing of the Alaskan pipeline, the dismantling of Exxon, or an end to highway construction to save gasoline, not to mention any more thoroughgoing transformation of our fossil fuel-based economy. Greenpeace launched its usual symbolic gestures, then sent home a photographer who was trying to assist organizing efforts by local fishermen. Still, the National Wildlife Federation gained 20,000 members in three weeks, the Sierra Club raised over $100,000 from a *New York Times* ad (most of which was given to local groups in Alaska), and the Wilderness Society gained $50,000 in unsolicited contributions.

Where the money goes varies tremendously from group to group. Some organizations funnel substantial funds to local activists and projects, while others maintain an increasingly closed corporate-style structure—a few actually do both. Clearly, the environmental movement may need to be analyzed in the same way we study other corporations: examining sources of funds, boards of directors, management structures, holdings, etc. A first perusal of the 1988 Annual Reports of the major environmental organizations revealed some interesting and occasionally surprising facts:

- The Sierra Club had a budget of $19 million, 64 percent of which came from member contributions. Their corporate matching gifts program, through which companies match employee contributions, brought in funds from ARCO, British Petroleum, Chemical Bank, Morgan Guaranty Trust, Pepsi, Transamerica, United Technologies, Wells Fargo, and others.

- The Audubon Society spent $38 million, with only $10 million coming from individual contributions. Corporate donors included the Rockefeller Brothers Fund, Waste Management Inc., General Electric, GTE, Amoco, Chevron, Dupont, and Morgan Guaranty Trust, with smaller donations (under $5,000) from Dow Chemical, Exxon, Ford, IBM, and Coca Cola.
- The Wilderness Society ($9 million, 50 percent from members) also listed Morgan and Waste Management among its corporate supporters. Their literature seeks to assure readers that the federal system of designated wilderness areas, for which they are a leading advocate, does not interfere in areas rich in oil, gas, and minerals, and advocates more intensive timber management in other places so that designated areas can be protected as wilderness without harming the timber industry.
- The National Wildlife Federation had a 1988 budget of $63 million, with only 22 percent coming directly from members (another 15 percent comes from the sale of magazine subscriptions to school children). Corporate donors include Amoco, ARCO, Coca Cola, Dow, Duke Power, DuPont, Exxon, GE, GM, IBM, Mobil, Monsanto, Tenneco, USX (formerly U.S. Steel), Waste Management, Westinghouse, and Weyerhaeuser. Matching grants came from Boeing, Chemical Bank, Citibank, Pepsi, the Rockefeller Group, United Technologies, and others.
- Greenpeace spent $22 million, almost entirely from "contributions and donations," including their extensive door-to-door and telephone canvassing operations. Telephone canvassing based in Seattle was moved to Boston in 1988, shortly after workers began organizing (with the aid of the local IWW) against workplace speedup and surveillance measures.
- The Natural Resources Defense Council ($11 million total) and Friends of the Earth (budget totals not listed) both received around 40 percent of their budgets from individual memberships and donations.

The well-endowed National Wildlife Federation (NWF) represents the pinnacle of Washington environmentalists' accommodation to the ways of corporate America. In 1982, NWF established its Corporate Conservation Council to "open dialogue" with "key industrial leaders" and further the idea that resource conservation is a key to "economic progress." Over half of NWF's corporate donors are members of the Council, which holds regular seminars and conferences to promote mutually-agreeable policy proposals. NWF has been a leading advocate for the myth of "sustainable development" in the Third World, and a champion of "debt-development" in the Third World, and a champion of "debt-for-nature" swaps, in which ecologically important lands in debtor countries are signed over to conservation groups in exchange for banks consenting to erase a portion of the country's debt. Last year, the Wildlife Federation offered a seat on its board of directors to Dean Buntrock, the head of Waste Management Inc., the world's largest processor of toxic chemical waste and the subject of numerous bribery and antitrust convictions, as well as countless environmental violations.

Enter William Reilly, whose nomination to head the U.S. Environmental Protection Agency (EPA) was almost universally applauded by environmentalists. Reilly's environmental credentials come from his work with the Conservation Foundation, another major proponent of "cooperation" between environmentalists and corporations. Reilly's group, and its offshoot, Clean Sites Inc., specialized in forging "compromise" solutions to environmental disputes, often at the expense of affected populations. According to reports from the Citizen's Clearinghouse for Hazardous Waste, a national alliance of grassroots anti-toxics groups, Reilly's organizations were often a willing cover for corporate interests, pushing "mediated" partial cleanups of Superfund sites and helping corporations minimize their liability for waste site cleanups. Some of this work was carried out in collaboration with former EPA chief William Ruckelshaus, who now heads BFI, the nation's second largest waste disposal and processing company. Says Ruckelshaus, "In a curious way, the strongest supporters of a forceful EPA are the industries it regulates. They want government to set reasonable standards and they want the public to know they are being enforced." He has clearly reaped the rewards of his own legacy of selective enforcement.

"A first perusal of the 1988 Annual Reports of the major environmental organizations revealed some interesting and occasionally surprising facts."

In 1987, local opponents of a proposed toxic waste facility in North Carolina pressured the state to enact stronger wastewater discharge regulations that would effectively prevent construction of the facility. The federal EPA intervened to block the new regulations, claiming they violated the state's responsibility under the federal Superfund act to devise a plan for managing hazardous waste. Citizen lobbyists from North Carolina collected testimony from lawmakers showing that the state was not violating any federal laws, and Reagan's last EPA Administrator, Lee Thomas, chose to back down. When Reilly took over in early 1989, two senior EPA officials allege that he met with waste industry executives and was convinced to reopen hearings challenging the North Carolina law. The two officials have filed criminal charges against Reilly in the case, having produced evidence for a meeting and a subsequent cover-up. The meetings were initiated, according to the Citizen's Clearinghouse, by none other than National Wildlife Federation present Jay Hair. "Cooperation" between industry and environmentalists has indeed come full circle.

Granted, this seems an extreme example of collaboration between environmentalists and polluting corporations. But as "responsible" environmentalists (no "extremists" need apply) increasingly covet their seats in Washington policy circles, and increasingly identify with those business and government interests that grant them their ostensible place in the power structure, such abuses are increasingly likely. As always, defenders of these practices argue "effectiveness," claiming that access to the corridors of power enables them to work more effectively for the environment. However, as the representatives of official environmentalism have become increasingly isolated from grassroots activists, as official environmentalism becomes increasingly "safe" and nonconfrontational, and as the movement shies further away from consideration of the underlying causes of environmental destruction, would-be environmental power brokers become increasingly obligated apologists for the system that both confers status and readily takes it away.

Examining The Record

Just how effective have environmentalists been over the years? If the country and the planet were significantly cleaner today than five or 10 or 20 years ago, a few compromises along the way might be justified. The record, unfortunately, suggests otherwise.

One of the most comprehensive assessments of the successes and failures of the environmental movement to date is a 1987 *New Yorker* piece by Barry Commoner. Interestingly, a 1988 article in *Fortune* magazine, which set out to assess environmental progress, calls a far more optimistic tune. While Commoner saw a failure of environmental regulation except in those limited cases where basic changes in production processes were ordered, *Fortune* declares the past two decades of environmentalism a success, setting the stage for a glowing new era of environmental cooperation based on market incentives and tradeable pollution "credits." Let us compare.

According to Commoner, the concentrations of many major air pollutants were reduced moderately in the 1970s, only to level off, or in many cases increase, in the 1980s. Carbon monoxide levels increased over the past decade, while levels of sulfur dioxide, the major contributor to acid rain, remained nearly constant. Nitrogen oxides, which contribute to smog formation in cities, have increased even since 1970, as automobile ownership (and also the use of synthetic nitrate fertilizers) continues to rise. *Fortune*, on the other hand, celebrates 20 to 40 percent declines in a few pollutants since 1970 (before which there were virtually no pollution regulations) as a sign of continuing progress.

Water pollution has continued to worsen too, as growth in polluting industries has outstepped improvements due to mandated sewage treatment and other technical fixes. While *Fortune* claims that Lake Erie has "come back to life," Commoner cites an EPA study showing that the number of biologically suffocated shoreline sites continued to rise, while fish populations in the lake have not significantly recovered. Commoner cites a 1982 survey of lakes, which revealed improvements in less than three percent of total lake area nationally. Meanwhile, *Fortune* cites over 200,000 miles of newly "swimmable and fishable" rivers. Though there have been some visible improvements due to improved sewage treatment and some reductions of phosphate levels, making a river swimmable does not mean it has regained its ecological integrity. In the Northeast, hundreds of popular fishing areas are still close to biological exhaustion, but are stocked annually with trout and other popular sport fish, which can no longer reproduce on their own. *Fortune* celebrates a 94 percent decline in ocean dumping of industrial waste—surely not a voluntary change on industry's part—but admits a 60 percent increase since 1970 in the ocean dumping of sewage sludge.

Commoner cites the still-growing proliferation of toxic chemicals, particularly from the petrochemical industry, as well as increasing levels of radioactive materials in the air. Only those radioactive components, such as Strontium 90, which are primarily associated with now-banned atmospheric weapons tests, have fallen significantly in the past 25 years. It is also clear to most activists that the overall condition of our continent's forests, range lands, wetlands, and prairies continues to deteriorate at astounding rates, even as the number of officially designated wilderness areas increases.

Commoner contrasts this rather dubious environmental record to those few cases where pollutants were banned outright, rather than merely "controlled"—reminiscent of the difference between arms control and disarmament, in a way. The harmful effects of lead, DDT, and PCBs on both people and wildlife have been nearly eliminated, as production and widespread use of these substances have been halted by law. PCB contamination continues to be a problem largely around abandoned factories and dump sites, which nine years of the federal Superfund have hardly begun to address. Real environmental improvements, argues Commoner, require a willingness to ban dangerous products outright, a measure which both saves lives and points to the need for more direct social intervention in production decisions and technological choices. Clearly, we also need a movement powerful enough to mandate such changes over the resistance of corporate managers and their allies.

The voices of corporate America, of course, continue to say otherwise, asserting that the costs of pollution prevention and cleanup are already too great. Lax environmental laws have joined cheap labor as a leading rationale for moving production overseas, as Third World governments, caught in the trap of indebtedness, often choose to ignore the ecological and health consequences of pollution. Movements against industrial pollution have appeared in India, where the Bhopal disaster brought a powerful message about the dark side of industrialization, but most nations suffering the burdens of neocolonial economics have been reluctant to make waves.

"...as official environmentalism becomes increasingly "safe" and nonconfrontational, and as the movement shies further away from consideration of the underlying causes of environmental destruction, would-be environmental power brokers become increasingly obligated apologists for the system that both confers status and readily takes it away."

In the U.S., the cost of pollution controls remains relatively small compared to other factors in the economy. A 1984 study placed total pollution control expenditures at $65 billion, or 1.8 percent of that year's Gross National Product. Military expenditures, by comparison, approach 10 percent or more of GNP. Of the $65 billion, only $40 billion was in the form of direct expenditures by business, with the remainder divided between government and consumers. *Fortune* quotes a higher figure of $78 billion a year for pollution control costs in the late 1980s. If one could estimate additional public health costs due to smog, unsafe drinking water, airborne carcinogens and teratogens (chemicals that cause birth defects), and the like, one might come up with a figure in the same ballpark. Try to quantify the damage to other living beings and to ecosystems, the loss of irreplaceable natural resources, depleted farm and forest soils, increases in genetic defects, declining bird and fish populations, etc., and their $78 billion begins to look like the proverbial spit in the ocean.

The costs of pollution controls are not evenly distributed through the economy, however. The most polluting industries—energy production, mining, oil refining, minerals processing, petrochemicals—pay the most for pollution control equipment and complain the loudest. Energy and chemical industries led the corporate reaction against environmental controls during the Reagan years. According to Jim O'Connor (of the journal *Capitalism, Nature, Socialism*), pollution controls and worker safety accounted for 40 percent of total capital expenditures in the copper industry in the mid-1970s, and 90 percent of construction cost increases for coal-fired power plants were due to government-mandated pollution controls. Stiffer safety requirements for nuclear power plants enacted after Three Mile Island—partly to appease a growing and increasingly militant anti-nuclear movement—helped make future nuclear power projects prohibitively costly.

The Changing Atmosphere Of Business

From an environmental standpoint, mandated pollution controls are an attempt to charge industries with the real costs of operation—to begin to internalize, in the lingo of environmental economists, the "externalities" of production that were once freely dumped on the shoulders of workers, nearby residents, and local and global ecosystems. Rather than shy away from these economic impacts, the ecology movement needs to articulate a social and political agenda that puts the current practices of industrial capitalism in historic perspective, and offers a clear alternative to the blind pursuit of economic growth.

Future environmental threats such as the greenhouse effect will necessitate a growing commitment to both environmental controls and changes in production in coming years. Atmospheric changes due to the greenhouse effect have already severely impacted global food suplies and increased the severity, and the human toll, of tropical storms; the weather is more than just a little strange these days. In the fall of 1989, *The New York Times* cited new economic studies predicting that the costs of reducing greenhouse gas emissions, especially carbon dioxide, could approach the level of current military spending over the next century. Increases in energy efficiency amounting to one percent per year could cut the figure in half, and alternatives to fossil fuels would cut it in half again. Both these measures embody socially desirable goals for a wide variety of reasons, but corporate think tanks are already working to rationalize not spending the money. Bush administration representatives joined their Soviet and Japanese counterparts in 1989 in blocking an international agreement to cut greenhouse emissions to 1988 levels by the year 2000. What we need, according to one Harvard economist, is "the will and technical ability to adapt to radically different weather." "The symbol of the greenhouse effect," paraphrases the *Times*, "cannot be allowed to obscure the dimensions of the perplexing, high-stakes problem that lies beneath." High-stakes indeed.

7

Environmental Democracy Is The Planet's Best Hope

Barry Commoner

It is a harsh irony that, in most nations of the industrialized world, both ordinary citizens and corporate executives look to government to satisfy their oft-conflicting interests. Not surprisingly, it is the latter who mostly frequent the corridors of the bureaucracy, rubbing shoulders, greasing palms, and winning out. Taking a hard look at the successes and failures of society as a whole in attempting to stop the destruction of people and planet, veteran environmental writer Barry Commoner comes up with some clear answers. Stopping problems at the source rather than trying to regulate them is essential, he says. And social control over the means of production, by grassroots groups from the environmental, civil rights, women's and peace movements, is the only way forward to a deep green future.

It's not simply the environmental movement that has failed in the 20 years since the first Earth Day. The government programs also have failed. The approach strategy taken by the U.S. Environmental Protection Agency (EPA) and all of the state environmental regulatory groups has been wrong. It hasn't worked. As a result, there's been very little improvement in the environment, and certain things have gotten worse.

This isn't just a hand-waving conclusion on my part. It's based on actual numbers. Look at the changes in emissions and pollutants. In 1970, the Clean Air Act Amendments called for a 90 percent reduction in urban levels of carbon monoxide, hydrocarbon, and ozone, setting a 1977 deadline for achieving this goal. In 1977, with compliance not even in sight, the deadline was moved to 1982. When that was missed, the deadline was delayed once more to December 31, 1987. Now, with nearly

100 million people breathing substandard air in urban areas that are still in non-compliance, the deadline may be extended up to 25 years *more!*

"The moral is, controls don't work. When a pollutant is attacked at its point of origin, it can be eliminated. Once produced, it's too late."

In a very few instances, we have succeeded. These allow us to examine the specific reasons for environmental success or failure. The answer is simple: if you don't put something into the environment, it's not there. Air emissions of lead have declined by 86 percent because much less lead is now added to gasoline and therefore that much less lead is contaminating the environment. The environmental levels of DDT and PCB have dropped sharply because their production and use have been banned. Mercury is much less prevalent in the environment bcause it is no longer used in manufacaturing chlorine. Strontium 90 has decayed to low levels because the United States and the Soviet Union have had the simple wisdom to stop the atmospheric bomb tests that produce it.

The moral is, controls don't work. When a pollutant is attacked at its point of origin, it can be eliminated. Once produced, it's too late.

The strategy has been to say, "OK, we've got these cars and power plants and so on that produce pollutants. We're not going to change them; we're just going to tack on control devices: scrubbers, catalytic converters, things like that." Such controls are ultimately self-defeating. To begin with, the effect of a control device is never complete. An exhaust-control system on a car does not trap all the carbon monoxide produced, but, at best, only about 90 percent of it. Besides, the effectiveness of the catalyst rapidly declines with use. Finally, in a number of cases, there's no way to use a control. You can't put a filter on agricultural pollution; there's no pipe out of which runoff nitrate fertilizer comes, because it comes out of every inch of the riverbank.

In other words, don't try to deal with the symptoms but with the cause. Our big mistake is that we've been putting on Band-Aids instead of going to the origin of the problem.

Most of these technologies were introduced after World War II and without any consideration of their environmental impact: the new, large, high-powered, smog-generating cars; the shift from fuel-efficient railroads to gas-guzzling trucks and cars; the substitution of many non-biodegradable and hazardous petrochemical products for biodegradable and less-toxic natural products; the substitution of chemical fertilizers for crop rotation and manure, and of toxic synthetic pesticides for ladybugs and birds.

We now know how to clean up the environment: alter the technologies of production. That means we have to introduce the social interest in environmental quality into the decision-making process that governs production technology.

There we run into a very serious problem. In our economic system, that decision process is totally under private control. A corporation's legal obligation is not to the nation but to its stockholders. Its decisions are made in the private interest, and that interest is maximizing profit.

So we now have to confront the clash between our economic ideology, which is capitalism, and the new idea that social interest in environmental quality must now intrude into this private province.

What is important here is social control, not of every single piece of production but of the crucial ones. Clearly, society has to say, "Build cars that do not produce smog." But it doesn't have to say how to make the wheels.

There are many positive examples of the social interest coming into play in an environmental debate. My favorite one is what happened with Alar. The EPA knew it was carcinogenic but didn't do anything. The National Resource Defense Council issues a report that says the levels in apples and apple juice are too high and should be reduced. That's another example of the control strategy, of course.

But then mothers hear all this, decide they're supposed to feed their kids healthful food, and stop buying apple juice and apples. Sales go way down; the growers scream; and Uniroyal, the company that produces Alar, takes it off the market.

That's what I call environmental democracy. Environmental democracy is responsible for essentially killing the nuclear power industry. The people said "We don't want this"—loudly enough that the industry had to put so many controls on it that they priced it out of the market. The big upsurge in recycling is a result of environmental democracy, of public opposition to incinerators.

There's value in individual actions if they orient you toward a social act. In other words, instead of just using string shopping bags yourself, work to have a law passed to ban the plastic ones. There are several hundred towns in Italy that have done this.

I urge people to find a social mechanism for dealing with the problem that's bothering them. Otherwise, the personal act may be a way of avoiding the social act—a form of escapism.

Take recycling as a marvelous example. A lot of environmentally minded people say, "Let's have a law that requires 25 percent recycling."

Is that good? No, it's bad. Why? Because if you pass a law for 25 percent recycling, you're guaranteeing 75 percent incineration. If you're doing recycling to feel good, 25 percent is great. If you're doing recycling to solve the trash problem, go for the maximum possible amount. In a pilot test in East Hampton, Long Island, we achieved 84.4 percent recycling.

"...the environment is only part of the problem. The other parts are jobs, poverty, discrimination—and they're all connected at the same point: the governance of the means of production."

Ecological metaphors like string shopping bags or planting trees can be used to get rid of personal guilt. They don't provide solutions, and, in some cases, they interfere with the solutions. Look, the problem is not in your head or my head. It's in the corporate boardrooms. That's where pollution begins.

The environmental movement has split in two. The old-line groups in Washington live by the control strategy. Their bread and butter are legislation and standards. More recently, they're negotiating with corporations as to what levels of pollution are acceptable.

The cutting edge of the environmental movement now is the grassroots groups. There are now 5,000 to 6,000 citizens' groups in towns and cities all over the country. They aren't "environmentalists" per se; they're simply people concerned with such problems as incineration and waste dumps, who are acting on them. They have adopted the prevention strategy and are ready to go head-to-head against the corporations. Now there are federations of these groups.

In a number of cases, the old-line national organizations have lost their influence locally and have even stood in the way of what really needs to be done. Here in New York, the Natural Resources Defense Council and the Environmental Defense Fund worked with the sanitation department in promoting incineration, whereas the people in the community were fighting it.

The environmental movement will not by itself solve the environmental problem; it can't, because that problem involves a fundamental political issue that can only be resolved by everybody. The great virtue of the environmental movement is that it illuminates this issue more readily than many other ways of looking at it. You see, the environment is only part of the problem. The other parts are jobs, poverty, discrimination—and they're all connected at the same point: the governance of the means of production. How can women and minorities get paid as well as white males? By gaining some governance of the source of our wealth, the system of production. So the environmentalists need to find common ground with the civil rights movement, the women's movement, the peace movement.

This is our chance; the situation is ripe. The ecologically sound technologies exist. There's world-wide concern about the environment. This innate democratic sense that people have is just bursting out everywhere. There are incipient movements in the right direction. And most important, really, there's the opportunity for getting the funds needed to make the ecological transition. They can only be gotten from the military budget; and with some disarmament already, and more happening fast, the military budget is up for grabs.

8

The Trouble With Earth Day

Kirkpatrick Sale

For many people across North America, Earth Day 1990 was an opportunity to imprint the green idea deep in the collective psyche. As a symbol of a new Earth consciousness, this 20th anniversary of the first Earth Day celebrated with great fanfare the widely-felt will to do things right by the Earth. But was it merely an expression of will? What are the chances that it actually propelled industrial culture along the road to genuine sustainability? From amidst the razzmatazz of Earth Day preparations in New York, bioregionalist Kirkpatrick Sale thinks that, when the dust has settled, little will be different. Worse, the (all of a sudden, big) business of hyping green business might finally have outgreened the greens themselves....

Imagine that a small child with many bruises is brought into a doctor's office and the physician is told that she has been repeatedly beaten. The first question to be asked is surely, Where does it hurt? with an inspection and remedies to follow. But it would be only the most callous and unethical doctor who would refrain from asking a series of other questions: How did it happen? Who did it? When? How long has this been going on? Why? How can we prevent it from happening again?

Imagine, then, that a society understands it is suffering from multiple environmental assaults of great seriousness. The first question it would ask itself is surely, Where does it hurt? and, assuming it to be a rational society, it would order an inspection and provide remedies, and swiftly and efficiently, too. But it would be only the most insensitive and basically self-destructive society that would refrain from asking a similar series of subsequent questions—in particular, Who did it? Where? Why? How can we prevent it from happening again?

In general the environmental organizations in this country and the official agencies that have grown up in response to them have not, over

57

the past two decades, gotten beyond the most elemental Where-does-it-hurt? questions; certainly they have not raised the deeper, subsequent questions or demanded the still deeper answers. Earth Day 1990, I regret to say, for all its ballyhoo and good intentions, has moved not one step out of that mire.

Earth Day 1990, the principal organization behind Earth Week, April 16-22, does ask, Where does it hurt? often and loudly, and its answers are the by-now-familiar litany: global warming, ozone depletion, deforestation, overpopulation, pollution of air and water, toxic waste, nuclear energy, overflowing landfills, resource depletion, acid rain, chemical poisoning. And it forthrightly confronts the question of how to fix those problems. On that basis it has set up a three million dollar operation with a national headquarters, fifteen regional offices, an agenda of 3,000 events and an occasion that will bring more crowds, media attention, political hype, celebrities and T-shirt sellers to environmental issues than any other in the nation's history.

But it is an operation—however well meaning, however many good people involved—that is, at its core, a shuck. For after telling us where it hurts, it gives us only the most simplistic sorts of remedies. Its first is personal "life-style" Band-Aids for hemorrhaging wounds and do-it-yourself surgery; its second is the nostrum of federal laws and regulations, providing the patient with more of the kind of cures that created the disease. And it never gets around to asking—much less proposing answers for—those fundamental questions this society must be forced to face: Who, really, is causing the degradation and destruction of the environment? How can they be stopped, and stopped short, not just "regulated" and "overseen" and reformed? Why has society allowed this to go on, to the point that all oxygen-dependent species, including humans, are imperiled, and why do we seem powerless to prevent it? What would it take to accomplish the serious, wrenching, full-scale readjustments that in fact are necessary to save the Earth, including reduced standards of living, consumption and growth; severe population reduction; and a new, modest, regardful relationship with the Earth and its species? Who is going to carry this literally vital message to the American people? And *when*? For the time, as every new crisis lets us know, is later than we think.

*

Let me be specific. Earth Day has four fundamental problems that to me seem to undermine its chance to create effective change and in some ways threaten to make it counterproductive.

First, like the rowdydow of books and articles over the past year since *Time*'s Planet-of-the-Year klaxon call, Earth Day's primary emphasis is on individual responses: "what *you* can do" to stop ozone depletion or rain forest destruction.

Look, I am as responsible as most eco-citizens: I bike everywhere; I don't own a car; I recycle newspapers, bottles, cans and plastic; I have a vegetable garden in the summer; I buy organic products; and I put all vegetable waste into my backyard compost bin, probably the only one in all of Greenwich Village. But I don't at the same time believe that I am saving the planet, or in fact doing anything of much consequence about the various eco-crises around us. What's more, I don't even believe that if "all of us" as individuals started doing the same it would make any but the slightest difference, and then only of degree and not—where it counts—of kind.

"Nothing less than a drastic overhaul of this civilization and an abandonment of its ingrained gods—progress, growth, exploitation, technology, materialism, humanism and power—will do anything substantial to halt our path to environmental destruction."

Leave aside ozone depletion and rain forest destruction—those are patently corporate crimes that no individual actions will remedy to any degree. Take, instead, energy consumption in the U.S.. In 1987 (the most recent figures) residential consumption was 7.2 percent of the total, commercial 5.5 percent and industrial 23.3 percent; of the remainder, 27.8 percent was transportation (about one-third of it by private car) and 36.3 percent was electric generation (about one-third for residential use). Individual energy use, in sum, was something like 28 percent of total consumption. Therefore, although you and I cutting down on energy consumption would have some small effect (and should be done), it is surely the energy consumption of industry and other large institutions such as government and agribusiness that needs to be addressed first. And it is industry and government that must be forced to explain what their consumption is for, what is produced by it, how necessary it is and how it can be drastically reduced. They need an Earth Day more than we do.

The point is that the ecological crisis *is* essentially beyond "our" control, as citizens or householders or consumers or even voters. It is not something that can be halted by recycling or double-pane insulation. It is the inevitable by-product of our modern industrial civilization, dominated by capitalist production and consumption and serviced and protected by various institutions of government, federal to local. It cannot possibly be altered or reversed by simple individual actions, even by the actions of the millions who will take part in Earth Day—and even if they all went home and fixed their refrigerators and from then on walked to work. Nothing less than a drastic overhaul of this civilization and an abandonment of its ingrained gods—progress, growth, exploitation, technology, materialism, humanism and power—will do anything substantial to halt our path to environmental destruction, and it's hard to see how the life-style solutions offered by Earth Day will have an effect on that.

What I find truly pernicious about such solutions is that they get people thinking they are actually making a difference and doing their part to halt the destruction of the Earth: "There, I've taken all the bottles to the recycling center and used my string bag at the grocery store; I guess that'll take care of global warming." It is the kind of thing that diverts people from the hard truths and hard choices and hard actions, from the recognition that they have to take on the larger forces of society—corporate and governmental—where true power, and true destructiveness, lie.

And to the argument that, well, you have to start somewhere to raise people's consciousness, I would reply that this individualistic approach does not in fact raise consciousness. It does not move people beyond their old familiar liberal perceptions of the world, it does nothing to challenge the belief in technofix or write-your-Congressperson solutions and it does not begin to provide them with the new vocabulary and modes of thought necessary for a true change of consciousness. We need, for example, to think of recycling centers not as the answer to our waste problems, as Earth Day suggests, but as a confession that the system of packaging and production in this society is out of control. Recycling centers are like hospitals; they are the institutions at the end of the cycle that take care of problems that would never exist if ecological criteria had operated at the beginning of the cycle. Until we have those kinds of understandings, we will not do anything with consciousness except reinforce it with the same misguided ideas that created the crisis.

*

Second, Earth Day is designed to be a weeklong media bash and not a long-range grassroots campaign with a clear and continuing political thrust. It is founded on the assumption, challengeable at best, that it was

Earth Day 1970 that was responsible for the establishment of the Environmental Protection Agency (EPA), passage of Clean Water and Clean Air acts and perhaps public support for environmental lobbies in Washington. So this time around the operating theory is that all you have to do is imitate the original event but make it bigger and you will automatically create, in the words of Earth Day 1990 chair Denis Hayes, "a citizens' army" for a "Decade of the Environment" and thus the constituency to force "a worldwide ban on chlorofluorocarbons by 1995," an 85 percent reduction in fossil fuel use by 2015 and an 80 percent reduction in acid rain.

There's nothing wrong with those goals, but why anyone would imagine that they could acquire a strong and active constituency as a result of a week of media-filtered eco-hype is somewhat puzzling. But this is the Earth Day strategy. Most of the three million dollars the organization is raising nationally and the one million dollars or so being raised locally is going to be spent on the events of Earth Week, culminating in the big marches and rallies of Earth Day. Very little is being devoted to building up a door-to-door outreach campaign that might take the movement beyond the already converted; very little to knitting existing neighborhood, watch-dog and environmental groups into a political network; and nothing at all, as far as I can tell, on the establishment of an organization for the continuing battle after the Earth Day tents are folded up.

"it is a fundamental tactical as well as philosophical error for the people working for substantial environmental transformation to make common cause with the very forces that are responsible for the eco-crisis in the first place."

Then too, the assumption behind Earth Day politics—when it is political at all—is that passing laws works to protect the environment. "We expect the world's governments," Hayes says, "to...actively begin addressing the wide array of urgent, important problems facing the planet." Well, in some cases passing laws can make a marginal difference, if the laws are tough, clear and easily enforceable—such as the ban on DDT (though it did not halt production of DDT entirely or its use overseas). But anyone who has studied the effect of the Clean Water and Clean Air acts in the past two decades cannot argue that they have been notably successful; anyone who has seen the miserable failure of the Superfund cleanups cannot assume that federal financing is effective;

anyone who has watched the generally bumbling and bureaucratized processes of the EPA cannot have a lot of confidence in its ability to control pollution, even when ordered to do so, in any serious way. Perhaps this legalistic strategy stems from the fact that so many of the people running Earth Day on the national level are lawyers, and that so many on its national board are politicians and lobbyists, but it's pretty late in the day to think that Congress or the EPA is the place to go for environmental change.

I do think it would be possible to take three million dollars and unlimited publicity and create an effective and tough-minded movement to identify the eco-criminals in our midst and work to put a stop to them, even to build support for the elements of an ecologically based society that would not permit such criminals to exist. But that takes time, commitment and a clear sense of values and goals, and Earth Day 1990 does not have enough of any of those. It's going in for the one-time splash, and that's unfortunate.

*

Third, I believe it is a fundamental tactical as well as philosophical error for the people working for substantial environmental transformation to make common cause with the very forces that are responsible for the eco-crisis in the first place or that are entirely wrapped up in the present lobbyist-lawyer- consultant-legislator-bureaucrat establishment that perpetuates it. This applies to corporations, of course, and to government agencies at all levels, but it applies also to the political and environmental do-goos who try to picture themselves as cleaner and greener than thou.

To their credit, the Earth Day organizers have not simply raised money from any corporation hoping to buy a good environmental image; they have also insisted that the sponsors show "some specific pro-environmental change in corporate behavior" and "an ongoing commitment to dialogue...with environmental advocates." The organizers have made explicit their commitment to the Valdez Principles promulgated in 1989 by environmentalists, which are supposed to make corporations "conduct their business as responsible stewards of the environment and seek profits only in a manner that leaves the Earth healthy and safe." Yet they have also gone after big corporations and wealthy individuals with great avidity—among the sponsors are Esprit, Church & Dwight, Shaklee and Coca- Cola—and they've put on their national board the heads of a dozen corporations and the likes of Ted Turner, Laurance Rockefeller, Vidal Sassoon and Jann Wenner. And they seem totally blind to the elemental ecological truth that, at bottom, the modern industrial economy is antithetical to ecological harmony; or, as Jeremy Seabrook has put it, "If it had been the purpose of human activity on Earth to bring the planet to the edge of ruin, no more efficient mechanism could have been invented than the market economy."

The opportunity exists, twenty years after the first Earth Day and twenty-eight years after the publication of *Silent Spring*, to raise some substantial questions about the nature of our industrial society: Who is producing the poisons of the field, who is cutting down the rain forests, who is causing acid rain, and why? But that would mean pointing fingers not only at conglomerate America but at the culture that sustains it, and this the Earth Day organizers cannot bring themselves to do, even if they had insight enough to recognize the problem.

It is the same undemanding willingness of Earth Day 1990 to work with those who will work with it that has allowed so many politicians and admen and media moguls and environmental do-goos to jump on its careening bandwagon. Already the national board is heavily laden with such types, and Earth Day itself will bring out still more, all nudging for a place in the limelight and a seal of good Earthkeeping. But just to show how risky a business this is, let's look at one man who graces the national board, Senator George Mitchell. He's the fellow who only recently showed his colors again when he worked so hard to gut President Bush's already fatuous "clean air" bill, arranging a behind-the-scenes deal that could not have delighted the auto companies and the electric utilities more.

Perhaps more disturbing, though, is the way that the organizers have let the environmental lobbies swarm around Earth Day like fish in a feeding frenzy. These are not sinister organizations, of course, but inevitably, doing what they do, they are accomplices in the basically sham process of environmental protection run out of Washington and in the political structure that supports it. They foster the idea that environmental politics consists in passing laws in Washington, that it is the work of specialists and experts and that it does not have anything to do with economic concentration, market forces, control of resources, community disfranchisement or ecological blindness. And their notion of strategy, not by accident similar to Earth Day 1990s, is to press for life-style changes on the one hand and send in a "generous tax-deductible Citizen Sponsor contribution" on the other. It is time to leave those lobby professionals behind; time to move on.

*

Finally, and to me most distressing, the organizers and sponsors of Earth Day at all levels seem to have no awareness of any other endangered species than the human, any other crises than those that threaten human comfort and consumption. In all the Earth Day literature—and it is copious; let's not even think of the number of trees felled—I have found only two or three halfhearted phrases, like "help preserve wetland habitat" and "water diversion often leads to destruction of wildlife," that move beyond a single-minded anthropocentrism. Most of it is unembarrassedly about "the peril to our species" and the need for "public safety and human dignity" and suchlike.

"This is not a matter of passing laws or double- paning windows; this is a deep reordering of values, a new (and very old) way of understanding the Earth and its species as sacred, an ecological consciousness that goes right to the heart of our lives."

Each day of Earth Week, for example, has been given over to a separate environmental issue. They are, in order, energy efficiency, recycling, water conservation, alternative transportation, toxin information and outdoor recreation. Each one, as you can see, is wholly concerned with human problems, human systems, human safety and basically how (American) humans can go on living at the same material level over the long haul without messing things up for themselves. Nowhere on that list is there any consideration of what are thought to be animals' (or trees' or rivers') rights; nowhere any regard for the ongoing extinction of species caused by humans; nowhere a concern for the countless other species that are being threatened daily by the destruction and poisoning of habits; nowhere any thought given to the restoration of the natural systems of the living Earth and learning to live in them as the first people did. Above all, nowhere on the list is there found any consideration of wilderness, of the need for a healthy Earth to have places where humans don't intervene, where the full complexity and diversity of life are allowed to flourish unimpeded. All that the Earth Day people can see is something called—just think of the implications—"outdoors," and all they can think of doing there is human "recreation."

The reason this is important is that until the human understands itself as a species—"reapplies for membership in the biosphere," as the ecohistorian Thomas Berry has put it—it will never stop treating the Earth and its treasures ("resources") as the rightful food for its omnivorous maw, will never stop acting as if it owns the Earth and has the right of "dominion over" its species. This is not a matter of passing laws or double-paning windows; this is a deep reordering of values, a new (and very old) way of understanding the Earth and its species as sacred, an ecological consciousness that goes right to the heart of our lives. Without it no profound changes will come, or last.

It was perhaps unrealistic of me to have expected that even such a clearheaded fellow as Denis Hayes would have come to embrace the very challenging concept of biocentrism (or ecocentrism, if you will) for Earth Day, or that, if he had, he would have been able to make it understood by the likes of Ted Turner and George Mitchell, not to mention the innumerable directors and staff members around the country. But Earth Day's overwhelming concentration on human peril and human survival still came as a bit of a surprise to me, I must admit, and a disappoinment. (Could the reason for this failure have something to do with the fact that only 17 percent of Earth Day 1990's national board are women, who are traditionally more sensitive here?) It shows what a long way we have to go before we achieve that essential alteration of values and perceptions that must come before we begin the work of transforming our civilization from the industrial to the ecological.

The occasion might best be used to start asking the right questions. One day devoted to Where-does-it-hurt? is all right, but only if it leads to Who? and Why? and How often? and above all, What will it take to stop it? Those are questions that we have to begin asking ourselves and the politicians, lobbyists, C.E.O.'s and powers-that-be in every dimension of our lives.

9

How Green Is Your Company? —A Corporate "Green Rating"

Guy Dauncey

The willingness of some companies to vault on to the green bandwagon, to portray a green image when their practices are far from environmentally or socially sound, and to exploit the media hype around "greenness" to the hilt, has led to much confusion and cynicism in many people's minds. Do we, as a result, mistrust all companies, as a consequence? Clearly not. But how we go about discriminating a veneer of green from the deep green, genuine article becomes a challenge. Guy Dauncey, a writer and consultant recently re-located to British Columbia from England, here begins the task of setting a framework within which we might judge the extent of a company's greenness. In the process, he outlines how genuinely concerned business people might ensure that they are moving toward "light green", at the very least.

The corporate and small business world is caught in a dilemma. Some people say, "You are responsible for all this mess." Others say, "We may not like the mess, but we don't want to lose our jobs." Some say, "We've got to stop producing and consuming so much, and cut back on growth." Others say, "If your products are environmentally harmful, we are going to stop buying them." The shareholders say, "If you don't maintain the value of our shares, we'll sell out," and the Board says, "If you don't produce good quarterly returns, we'll cut your pay (or fire you)."

From the perspective of the global environment, the issue is simply "Get sustainable—100 percent environmentally sustainable." But what does this mean? It does not mean "no growth" as such—everyone wants the growth of organic farms and recycled paper companies, for instance.

The answer is to *get specific*: what *exactly* is the problem?

"Getting specific" means drafting up a detailed agenda, spelling out the specific areas where change is needed in order for your company to move towards a way of operating that is 100 percent environmentally sustainable.

Specific things companies can do to accelerate their "greening:"

* Establish a cross-departmental Environmental Action Team.

* Appoint an Environmental Vice-President with a brief to get things moving in the direction of cleaning up the company's act.

* Commission a full Environmental Audit to check for environmental excellence and sustainability (not just for contract compliance).

* Produce a staff questionnaire seeking responses to specific environmental issues, and inviting suggestions about particular actions the company might take, or new products they might develop.

* Produce a customer questionnaire along similar lines.

* Hold cross-company Environmental Hearings or Forums to engage the staff's concern and involvement and to get their ideas.

* Instruct every department to set up its own Environmental Working Party, with a brief to come up with ideas as to how they could become more "green."

A "Green Rating" would enable companies to establish an outline agenda for action, while simultaneously allowing the public to reward good conduct. What follows is a crude beginning to such a system— crude because the quiz below does not allow for the many sectors of the economy, and the different activities that businesses in each sector engage in. For example, resource industries—such as forestry—are not included; and industries producing huge amounts of (toxic) waste— such as the pulp and paper industry—are compared equally to businesses which may produce only office waste paper. So total scores should act only as a guide. Also, the quiz assumes that it will be answered honestly, with no deviousness—perhaps a dangerous assumption.... It consists of a 20 point do- it-yourself questionnaire. Up to five points can be scored for each question, giving a maximum of 100 points for total environmental sustainability. Points are scored as follows:

5 = An unconditional "Yes"

4 = Yes, in most situations

3 = Yes, to some degree

2 = We have begun to work on this issue

1 = We probably ought to look at this issue

0 = We do not think this is a relevant issue

A Company Green Quiz

1. COMPANY POLICY

Does your company have a clear policy statement from the Board referring to the need to achieve environmental excellence and sustainability in every field of activity?

2. PLANNING, ORGANIZATION AND COMMUNICATIONS

Does your company have clear instructions regarding managerial and line management roles and responsibilities for implementing and reporting on environmental policy? Do you have open communications channels regarding environmental issues with employees, customers, shareholders, suppliers, the local community and the public at large? (Newsletters, videos, environmental procedures, manuals, etc.)

3. COMPANY ACTIVITIES AND PRODUCTS

Are your company's main activities and products of a nature such that they are inherently sustainable, ecologically; and if not, are you taking steps to ensure that they become so?

4. ENERGY USE (re: the Greenhouse Effect)

Does your company have a policy designed to minimize its use of energy, to invest in the most efficient energy-savings technologies, and to utilise sustainable energy sources wherever possible?

5. MATERIALS

Could your company's use of materials be sustained indefinitely without undue harm to the environment; and where not, are you actively pursuing or encouraging an active search for alternatives?

6. WASTE

Does your company produce waste products which are harmful to the environment, which are toxic, non-biodegradable, unsightly or excessively noisy; and if so, do you have a policy to recycle or dispose of them in a sustainable manner, or to design your production processes so as to eliminate them?

7. ACCIDENT PROTECTION AND EMERGENCY PROCEDURES

Does your company have procedures to minimize the occurence of accidents, with clearly laid-down and rehearsed rapid-response emergency procedures? (Toxic escapes, oil spills, fire hazards.)

8. PRODUCT TESTING

Does your company avoid all product-testing which involves cruelty to animals; if not, do you have a policy to research alternative methods of testing, or to withdraw those products from production?

9. PURCHASING POLICY

Does your company require of its suppliers, contractors and deliverers that the products supplied, along with the methods of production and delivery, meet a high standard of environmental excellence and sustainability; where not, do you have a policy to seek alternative suppliers, or to work with existing suppliers and contractors to develop environmentally sustainable systems?

10. TRANSPORT

Does your company have a policy designed to maximize the environmental cleanliness and efficiency of its fleet, and of the transportation systems utilized by sub-contractors to deliver goods and supplies, and to minimize the need for transport as a whole of both suppliers and employees? (Car-sharing programs, vehicle-use monitoring, company bus/rail passes, company bikes, low fuel-consumption vehicles, etc.)

11. PHYSICAL SITES

Does your company have policies designed to ensure the maximum environmental safety, attractiveness and healthiness of its offices, buildings, factories, farms and sites? (Tree-planting, treatment for sick building syndrome, sustainable farming, beautification programs, site-restoration, etc.)

12. EMPLOYEE HEALTH

Does your company have policies designed to ensure that the fullest employee health and safety is maintained? (Safety training, protection against toxic materials, no-smoking programs, nourishing food, health checks, eyestrain checks for VDU operators, etc.)

13. INVESTMENT OF PENSION FUNDS AND CAPITAL SURPLUSES

Does your company invest its pension funds and capital surpluses in a way that has been screened for social and environmental responsibility? Where not, do you have plans to reinvest them accordingly?

14. TRAINING

Has your company set up the means to keep abreast of current environmental developments, and has it established appropriate environmental training courses for employees?

15. OVERSEAS OPERATIONS

Does your company have policies designed to ensure that overseas trading practices meet the same standards of sustainability pursued at home?

16. ENVIRONMENTAL MONITORING AND AUDITING

Has your company established procedures to monitor and audit key indicators concerning environmental performance, on a regular basis? (Use of materials, waste, transport, energy-use, etc.)

17. EMPLOYEE PARTICIPATION

Does your company have policies to encourage employee involvement in the pursuit of environmental excellence, to give appropriate rewards for significant contributions, and to encourage employees to become more environmentally aware?

18. CUSTOMER PARTICIPATION

Does your company have policies designed to encourage customers to become more environmentally aware? (Environmental labeling, recycling schemes, etc.)

19. CORPORATE SPONSORSHIP

Does your company give financial and other support to encourage the development of environmental initiatives in the community?

20. LONG-TERM PLANNING FOR SUSTAINABILITY

Does your company have a long-term development plan which aims to encourage environmental excellence and sustainability on the planet as a whole?

TOTAL SCORE:

Part Two

Making A Living
Or "Living A Making?"

I'm just trying to make a living," says the logger, in response to criticism about what he does for money. In a world where each must look out for themselves, competition for the bucks made from exploitation of one kind or another continues apace in spite of the warnings that we have gone too far. Making a living for most people means spending a large part of their time at work they don't like, often in unhealthy environments. Entire adult lives are spent as wage-slaves, with only evenings and weekends left for "real life", time spent with family and friends—a sad state of affairs for a social species whose well-being depends upon the quality of its social and cultural life. We have bought into a mythology based on materialism that says you can't count on people, that real security can only be bought, and where the sale of goods and services has replaced cooperation and sharing. This is what lies behind "making a living."

What if we took seriously the idea that if humankind were to continue to survive on this planet, it must find its place among the other species in the natural world? We would then perhaps be much more interested in "living a making"as proposed by Peter Berg, from Planet Drum Foundation. Turning around the usual phrase suggests a whole new way of being, that we might sculpt our daily lives to fit the particular circumstances of people and place, holding the long term viability of both very much at heart. It suggests, too, radically different ways of doing business that would support such efforts.

Returning to the metaphor from ecology, "living a making," might begin the process of replacing competition and self-interest with the well-being of the whole. What if, instead of the chaotic free-for-all of a society based on a "pioneering" mentality—marked by economic instability and rampant competition—communities began to make stable economies through cooperation, respectful self-government and equitable access to the gifts of this Earth? It is a beautiful, deep green image that emerges from a world not fundamentally motivated by profit (even "green profit"), but evolving from a profound respect

71

for the well-being of all life.

The contributions in Part Two point the way toward some of the characteristics of business that might prevail if we chose this path.

50 DIFFICULT Things You Can Do To Save The Earth

Compiled by Gar Smith

1. Bury your car.
2. Become a total vegetarian.
3. Grow your own vegetables.
4. Have your power lines disconnected.
5. Don't have children.
6. Restrict the population of motor vehicles.
7. Don't build cars.
8. Stop building roads.
9. Replace roads with homes, parks, and gardens.
10. Halt weapons production and exports.
11. Stop the sale, distribution, and export of cigarettes.
12. Send money to Brazil to provide urban jobs for impoverished workers now forced into the rainforests.
13. Blockade a lumber truck carrying old-growth trees.
14. Spend a month tree-sitting.
15. Try to live within the world average income ($1,250 a year).
16. Cut up your credit cards.
17. Unplug your television.
18. Undertake a "conservation Sabbath"—one day a week without consuming electricity or fuel.
19. Fast one day each week and send the money saved on food to help feed the hungry.
20. Adopt a homeless person.
21. Raise the minimum wage to a survival income.
22. Enact a maximum wage law.
23. Tie politicians' salaries to the average working wage.
24. Replace majority rule with proportional representation.
25. Replace the Electoral College with direct democratic elections.

26. Abolish the CIA and the National Security Act of 1949.

27. Pass a nature amendment to the U.S. Constitution.

28. Oust presidential adviser John Sununu.

29. Plant one new tree every day.

30. Go to jail for something you believe in.

31. Don't own pets.

32. Allow all beef-producing domestic cattle to become extinct.

33. Redirect the military budget to restoration work; convert weapons factories to peaceful research; retrain soldiers for ecological restoration.

34. Remove the U.S. Forest Service from under the Agriculture Department; place USFS, the Bureau of Land Management, and the Fish and Wildlife Service under the Environmental Protection Agency.

35. Consume only products produced within your bioregion.

36. Don't eat anything that comes in a package.

37. Don't buy anything that comes in a box.

38. Require operators and owners of nuclear power plants to live within one mile of the site.

39. Mandate federal recycling and institute a refuse tax on solid waste.

40. Pipe polluted water back into the water supplies of the companies that do the polluting.

41. Don't own anything that runs on batteries.

42. Hand over all excess packaging to a store manager on each visit to the grocery store.

43. Travel by bus, never by air.

44. Stop using toilet paper and Kleenex; use washable cloth.

45. Extend the life of your wardrobe by learning to make and mend your own clothes.

46. Give money to every single panhandler you meet.

47. Democratize your workplace; start a union or a collective.

48. Learn to farm.

49. Liberate a zoo.

50. Ask your boss if you can take a day off to work on healing the planet...with pay!

10

Bursting The Bottle:
Soap Selling For The '90s

Randy Hooper

One of the major problems with green consuming is that its field of view is very narrow. Are we really making a big difference buying our recycled motor oil in one litre "throwaway" plastic containers, or our unbleached toilet tissue in four-packs wrapped copiously in yet more plastic, for example? The garbage and landfill crisis is little better off from such "green" business practices, neither does the ozone layer benefit from any reduction in the burning of fossil fuels to get these products distributed continent-wide to market in the usual fashion. As an alternative, buying in bulk saves more than just money: it saves the environment, too. And while bulk-buying alone doesn't exactly make for a "deep green" society, the exercise of rethinking where we get our products from and how we sell them leads also to questioning what we get and whether we need such items.

Randy Hooper, who has been in the marketing business most of his life, believes there are far more radical alternatives to be explored by retailers and communities who want to get serious about deep green business. From his home on Saltspring Island in British Columbia, he's been crunching numbers and coming up with some startling results...

How do we translate a bottle of household spray cleaner into a bioregional, economic quiz? Simple. We're going to compare the real cost to a community, environmentally and economically, of buying one litre bottles of ready-to-use "national brand" cleaner as opposed to buying concentrated low, or no-name, brand cleaner in bulk in an old spray bottle you take to the store! Why? Very simply to show you just how huge the difference is, and then to draw some worthwhile conclusions about how thinking globally, but acting *and buying* locally, can make a measurable difference.

To make this analysis easy, we need a population of about 7500 people living in about 2500 houses. Saltspring Island has about that, so that's what I'll use. The people of Saltspring vary from minimalists without children, pets, cigarettes and animal fat in their lives and who use three teaspoons of baking soda annually for all their cleaning chores, to the antithesis: those who require 24 bottles of a pretty potent cleaner a year to get all that bacon grease off their stove vents, nicotine off their walls, etc.... On *average*, this varied population goes through four bottles a year per household. Those bottles sell for $3.00 plus tax, for an annual budget for Saltspring Island of $31,800 for full strength spray-on gunk remover. The fun is to figure out where that $31,800 goes!

Packaging, Petrochemicals and Profit-Perversity

There are three components here. First is the cost of the packaging, second the cost of getting the cleaner from the formulator to the final vendor, and third are the costs that must be covered in the retailer's mark-up. Let's start with packaging. The bottle costs 30 cents, the trigger 40 cents, one space in the cardboard box is about seven cents, labels on the front and back cost six cents, and the guy who puts them altogether (the bottler) charges a dime a bottle. So we're at 93 cents, and that's just the packaging. The packaging has involved the petrochemical industry which produces the plastics for the bottles, triggers and labels; the pulp and paper industry which is providing pulp for cardboard boxes; the metal industry which makes staples for the boxes, etc.; and the trucking industry which is likely moving that packaging over 1000 miles in total before it has anything in it.

"if a community of 7,500 people simply changed the way they bought one simple little product, that community would have an extra $19,558."

Now, that bottle of cleaner, once filled, labelled and boxed by the bottler, becomes a commodity to be reckoned with. Most likely it will be shipped to the "Eco Clean" warehouse, then by rail to national brokerage houses, then by truck to regional wholesalers, and/or cash and carry locations, or distribution centers for national retail chains. Then it will go by local delivery truck to retail stores. By now, with bottles produced in Connecticut, trigger sprayers produced in Granby, boxes produced in New Brunswick, and retailers selling the product on the Gulf Islands in British Columbia, some of that packaging has travelled five thousand miles. The manufacturer, national broker, regional wholesalers and cash and carry locations require good gross profit margins to cover advertising, sales reps, warehouse overhead, employment taxes, trade shows, warehouse and office staff, business taxes, plus national advertising, liability insurance, store listing fees, research, market testing, obsolete stock, shrinkage, shipping and warehouse damage, bad debt, office and accounting work, lawyers and accountants, and so on.

The landed cost at the local store is now $2.23. Of the $1.30 that's been added to the cost of the packaging, a few cents will go to marketing costs (trade shows, sales reps, etc.), two cents to liability insurance, five cents to transportation, plus another two cents in transportation and fuel taxes. It's going to cost 15 cents to pay for the overhead in at least three different warehouses, 34 cents for the labor and staff involved in moving, sorting, storing, invoicing, etc., and, with it, 14 cents in employment taxes, compensation, holiday pay, unemployment insurance, etc. There will be three cents in business and property taxes, eight cents in after-tax profit for the companies involved (that's a six percent return on investment), and five cents for the federal government in income taxes. At a wholesale price of $2.23 there's also (right now) an additional 30 cents in federal sales taxes. So this all adds up to $1.22. I ran the figures through twice and they just don't reach $1.30. Then I realized I hadn't built in the *actual* cost of the cleaner itself—eight cents. *Eight cents*? (Now this may be a bit low, and some cleaners may cost as much as 50 cents a litre, but they will also sell for more than three dollars a bottle!)

"$200 in fuel taxes, $2,700 in employment taxes, $300 in property/business taxes, $1,000 in income taxes and $4,800 in sales taxes. That's a total of $9,000 in taxes!"

Now the product arrives at a retail store, where over the year, if that store were the only one on Saltspring Island (which it isn't), it would have to deal with receiving, storing, racking, pricing and checking out 10,000 bottles, and *throw away* or maybe recycle 833 cardboard boxes. They have lots of costs too, including that weekly flyer that is duplicated in the local paper just in case Canada Post forgot to put one in your box! They contribute a couple of points to local charity, have their own little league team, provide free juice at community events... And they have to build in a margin for shoplifting, bad cheques, damaged and out of date stock, rent, lights, stolen grocery carts and huge amounts of liability insurance. Of the 77 cents they are going to make, 35 cents goes to their staff, and another 13 cents goes to government departments as employment taxes. Of the remaining 29 cents, 12 will pay for their overhead, three cents goes to marketing, two cents goes to insurance, seven is their after-tax profit, and five cents goes to the government as income taxes. Don't forget another 18 cents goes to the provincial government as sales tax.

Adding up the figures, I get a total of 57 cents per bottle staying in the community, and the other $2.61 going away, and staying away. Of the original budget of $31,800, $9,300 is going to pay for packaging, $800 pays for the raw materials, $3,400 pays for overhead and marketing, $400 goes to the insurance companies, $500 to the truckers, $6,900 goes to the people working at all those different companies, and all nine companies involved keep $1,500 of profit for themselves. There is also $200 in fuel taxes, $2,700 in employment taxes, $300 in property/business taxes, $1,000 in income taxes and $4,800 in sales taxes. That's a total of $9,000 in taxes!

So, when you buy your new bottle of cruelty-free, biodegradable green spray, in its shiny new plastic bottle, are you really making a difference? The argument which I hear (and agree with) from the makers of more suitable household cleaner, is that it appeals to those who have just decided that there is a problem and who want to become part of the solution. Will both these consumers, and community stores, be able to take the next step in the transformation?

The Bulk Barrel Alternative

If your local store brought in a 220 litre (45 gallon) drum of a highly concentrated soap, things would be a lot different. You would take in your own bottle, and they would stock it in a jug with a tap. They'd have to fill that jug with 17.5 litres of water every couple of days, and then add 2.5 litres of super concentrate pumped from the drum out the back. That soap would then still be concentrated enough for consumers to thin it down 6:1 with water at home, depending on the cleaning job.

Let's look at how the $31,800 spent on cleaner breaks down this time. The drum of super concentrate costs the store $2,300, and will produce, when water is added, 1760 litres of cleaner. Per litre, the soap is worth (and remember that it is still in concentrated form), about 50 cents. Per litre, there is six cents for transportation, three cents for packaging (that returnable drum and the jug in the store), nine cents for labor, one cent for insurance, 23 cents for after-tax profit, 16 cents for income tax, 18 cents for federal sales taxes, three cents for employment taxes, one cent for business tax and one cent for fuel tax.

The store is going to sell this cleaner for $6.36 a litre with tax, and people are going to buy one every year and a half because it's so concentrated. The big drum, when thinned down with water, will produce 1760 litres of soap, more than enough for a year if the 2,500 households buy one every 18 months. Now, I'm going to assume that the same amount of time will be spent having to fill up that jug every couple of days as dealing with pricing and stocking a couple of cases of bottled cleaner, and then dealing with the boxes. But, for this exercise, I've doubled the labor costs. I've assigned the same cost breakdown of the traditional bottled cleaner to the bulk cleaner on a per unit basis, not on a percentage basis.

"in total, $25,258 of the $31,800 stays in the community, as opposed to $5,700 the '80s way."

Back to the $31,800 that the community is going to spend on cleaner. The '90s way, I get $880 for the soap (nearly the same as for the cleaner sold in one litre bottles) $105 for transportation, $74 for packaging, $158 for production labor, $1,232 for retail store staff, $72 for insurance, $344 for overhead and marketing, $3,824 for profit, $3,330 for income taxes, $310 in federal sales tax, $547 for employment taxes, $317 for provincial sales taxes. That adds up to $11,193 of which $6,542 will go out of the community (most of which is taxes). And what of the other $20,706? It never got spent! So, in total, $25,258 of the $31,800 stays in the community, as opposed to $5,700 the '80s way.

There are a lot of numbers here, but I have tried to show you, somewhat meticulously, that Apply this bit of simple thinking to the effect on a community where stores sell bulk grain, bulk ketchup, bulk cookies, bulk cleaners, bulk motor oil, bulk popcorn, bulk peanut butter, bulk herbs, bulk cat and dog food, juice and milk on tap, etc... where the consumer really saves. I bought a 750 ml. jar of Skippy Natural Peanut Butter for $4.95 a year ago. I bought a 10 kg. pail a month later for $22.50 through a food co-op. By my arithmetic, that's one-third the price, and I got a nice re-usable pail into the bargain!

So there are great savings to be made by buying in bulk, not for any other reason than that the packaging accounts for a very measurable percentage of the cost.

The Environmental Impact

Now, let's add a whole new dimension to all this information. When that 220 litre drum of concentrate is used up, it can be re-used over and over again. It doesn't need to be recycled or thrown away. Compare that to the 10,000 one litre bottles—what happens to them? And to the cardboard boxes which your community has to de-tape, de-staple, flatten and bale, only to receive $20 a ton for them—in other words, recycling them at a loss!

What is the environmental impact of having to deal with all the paper shuffling, as nine or ten different companies, from the box maker, to the accountant in the grocery store, all have to deal with that bottle of soap, or the impact of all the transportation, asphalt, spent motor oil and non-renewable fuel resources that are involved?

What is the impact when we go to the store and buy bananas from Costa Rica, grapes from Chile, canned peaches from Australia, Brisling Sardines from Norway, Gouda from Holland, coffee from Columbia, tomato paste from Portugal?

Is buying Ecover Toilet Cleaner in a one-shot plastic bottle, imported from Belgium, really making any difference at all? As I mentioned above, in my opinion, *it is*, to those who are just realizing what it is to be "green," and maybe it's a golden opportunity to facilitate an easy "conversion" for those who won't believe the greenhouse effect exists until government starts to tax it.

Armed with the above information, sit down and figure out the savings to you and your community, financially and ecologically, if you used environmental common sense and applied it to the way you buy most commodities—trying to eliminate packaging, and buying products produced as close to you as possible. As I was the first time I went through this process, you might be amazed!

11

Seikatsu: Japanese Housewives Organize

Shigeki Maruyama

The notion that the planet can be saved by individuals consuming green products begs numerous questions ranging from the structure of business itself, through the manufacturing process, to the fact that buying green is for the most part a highly individualistic response. Cooperatives have been a frequently used means for people to move beyond conventional business forms, even if only to buy together in bulk or, in a more developed form, to own, manage and run their own enterprises.

In Japan, a group of housewives has taken the coop model several strides further forward to involve an environmental ethic, a philosophy that embraces all of life, and an active political role in local and national affairs. Run by a board of directors that comprises eighty percent women, the Seikatsu Club has been putting a broad range of progressive principles into practice successfully for many years, making the green product fetish pale by comparison.

Japanese society has undergone sweeping transformations since World War II. With the end of the war, the nation adopted a new constitution which introduced a democratic value system to the Japanese people for the first time. Rapid urbanization brought on the rise of the Japanese corporation and the advent of the nuclear family. And accelerated economic growth which clutched Japan in the 1960s has yet to let the nation out of its grip.

But Japan's so-called "economic miracle" brought on geographic, environmental and lifestyle changes that have not necessarily improved the quality of life here. Farmers flowed from the countryside into cities at the rate of 800,000-900,000 every year, and rural dwellers decreased by 51 percent from 11.95 million in 1965 to 5.88 million people in 1975. This trend has persisted over the last decade resulting in a farm population of less than five million people.

Meanwhile the new urbanites grew increasingly removed from the production process and more susceptible to mass media campaigns. the demand for standardized, visually appealing merchandise increased. In response, farmers across the nation took to using agricultural chemicals and chemical fertilizer to ensure a saleable crop. Urbanization took its toll on the environment in other ways as well. As industrialized Japan kowtowed to the needs of big business at the expense of natural resources, air and water pollution spread, resulting in atrocities like Minamata disease.

"We refuse to handle products if they are detrimental to the health of our members or the environment."

All over the country, Japanese worked long hours with few vacations for little pay. Eager to further spur incentive, in 1960 Prime Minister Hayato Ikeda promised to double personal income within ten years. Although he remained true to his pledge, the cost to the Japanese people was an annual inflation rate of 10 percent.

Motivated by the fundamental need to combat rising prices, in June 1965, one housewife from Tokyo's Setagaya district organized 200 women to buy 300 bottles of milk. Though it was not officially founded until 1968, in a sense, it was the Seikatsu Club's first collective purchase.

Principles of the Seikatsu Club

What started as a strategy to save money, however, gradually developed over the next 20 years into a philosophy encompassing the whole of life. In addition to cost-effective collective purchases, the club is commited to a host of social concerns, including the environment, the empowerment of women and workers' conditions.

The primary function of the Seikatsu Club is not to sell but to buy. Unlike most Japanese coops which distribute merchandise through their stores, the club delivers goods directly to its members. Primary products like rice, milk, chicken, eggs, fish and vegetables make up 60 percent of our total stock. Seasonings such as miso and soy, processed foods and general merchandise like powdered soup, clothing and kitchen utensils are also available.

In order to cope with rising competition with supermarkets and other cooperatives, many coops have sought to expand by decreasing investment and increasing dividends. But we believe that our business should be run by our own investments. This is part of the club's vision to reduce the division between producer, consumer and investor. When members join the coop, they make an initial investment of 1000 yen. This, supplemented by monthly contributions of 1000 yen, brings the average investment to roughly 47,000 yen per person, which is returned whenever a member leaves the coop.

Our investment strategy has been highly successful: although the membership (153,000) ranks ninth out of Japan's 700 coops, for instance, we are fourth in terms of investment capital which totals 7.5 billion yen. Because the point of investment is not profit, the club does not offer dividends to its members.

Respecting the Environment

We refuse to handle products if they are detrimental to the health of our members or the environment. Synthetic detergents, artificial seasoning and clothing made with fluorescents are all off limits, even if members make demands for them.

But our commitment to the environment is far more extensive than that. For one thing, the club gets safer produce by cooperating with local farmers. In return for asking them to use organic fertilizer and fewer chemicals, members buy a contracted amount of produce and agree to overlook physical imperfections if they exist. Members also assist farmers with the harvest when their labor is necessary.

We stand by the belief that housewives can begin to create a society that is harmonious with nature by "taking action from the home." And through our purchases and consumption, we are attempting to change the way that Japanese agriculture and fisheries are operated. As a symbolic gesture of societal responsibility for past crimes due to careless industrialization, we buy summer oranges from families with Minamata disease.

When the club cannot find products which meet our quality, ecological or social standards, we will consider starting our own enterprise. This can be illustrated by the two organic milk production facilities we currently run with local dairy farmers.

We also have an agreement with an organic agricultural coop in the Shounai district of Yamagata prefecture: beginning with rice in 1972, it gradually expanded to vegetables and fruit, and now accounts for 30 percent of our total purchases.

Buying directly from producers does more than merely eliminate the middleman's added distribution cost. It enhances cooperation and awareness by keeping consumers in touch with the production process.

Collective Buying

The Seikatsu Club utilizes a unique collective purchase system which relies on: a) advance orders, b) distribution and payment based on a "han" or group, c) the concept of "one product/one variety," which limits the availability of any given item to a single brand.

When the club first got its start, we studied various coop systems throughout Japan. Unable to find a method suitable to our needs, we developed our own original system: advance ordering. Once a month, members place orders one week before each purchase so that producers can plan in advance. This system also ensures freshness which means that preservatives are not necessary in our original brand food.

"We stand by the belief that housewives can begin to create a society that is harmonious with nature by *taking action from the home."*

Individual members have no real buying power in the Seikatsu Club. A "han," composed of 6-13 families, is the basic unit for collective purchasing, and must buy in bulk—a minimum of 15 cartons of milk or seven kilograms of eggs, for instance. Items sold in bulk include pork, processed meat, frozen seafood and vegetables.

An autonomous local group which makes purchasing and broader policy decisions, the "han" has been useful in increasing production and distribution efficiency, reducing cost and promoting cooperative labor within the group. Through encouraging members to participate freely and actively and to train and educate each other, the club is also striving to nurture self-management skills.

Coop staff deliver most goods in 1-1.5 ton trucks, while food requiring refrigeration is distributed by Taiyo Food Sales Company. Receipt and dispersal of merchandise and collection of orders, however, is handled by members. In the beginning of each month, order forms, catalogues and newsletters are distributed to "han" members by a member-on-duty. One week later, members pay for the previous month's order. The following week, advance orders are taken by another member-on-duty, and processed by computer. Milk deliveries, called "milk mail" are made twice a week. Eggs, pork, processed foods and seasonings are distributed once a week. All other goods including rice are distributed once a month.

Although most coops offer a wide range of merchandise, the club handles only 400 products in total. We believe that limiting quantity ensures quality; as a result we offer only one version of any given product. Soy sauce is produced in numerous sizes and shapes in Japan, but we provide nothing other than one litre glass bottles of thick soy. Through limiting variety, the club is able to streamline production and distribution. It also enables us to make special demands of producers—like leaving out preservatives.

The club also feels that limiting options cultivates creativity in daily life. We do not deal with salad dressing, for example, because we want to encourage members to make their own.

From Soap to City Council

Through the "Shounai Exchange," women from the Shounai coop joined the club's soap movement and succeeded in getting synthetic detergents off the shelves of their coop shops. As a result, "shirauo," a white fish sensitive to pollution, began to return to the town river.

Started in 1974, the club's soap movement offers a fine example of how "the kitchen" can provide an effective starting point for a political movement. After noticing cracked skin on their own hands and skin irritation on their babies, housewives began to question synthetic soaps and the club started purchasing natural soap from a local producer.

Roughly 60-70 percent of our members switched to natural soap. They took their fight to the local government level by organizing petition drives in Kanagawa, Chiba, Saitama and Hokkaido. Some local assemblies enacted legislation eliminating the use of synthetic detergents, but by and large the members were defeated—even though they managed to collect a total of 300,000 signatures. (Nationwide about 10 percent of the population is thought to use natural detergent.)

"Campaigning on the slogan, "Political Reform from the Kitchen," the club succeeded in getting 33 members elected on the municipal level."

Realizing that lack of experience contributed to their defeat, the club's members sought a more active role in politics. Most of our members are women, so most of the organizing impetus has come from housewives. In 1979, the first Seikatsu Club member (a housewife) was successful in getting elected as a representative in Tokyo's Nerima Ward. This initial success deepened the confidence of the club's female members. Campaigning on the slogan, "Political Reform from the Kitchen," the club succeeded in getting 33 members elected on the municipal level. Although the Seikatsu Club only sends about one or two members to a quorum of 30-100 people, the success of our "housewives" has attracted the attention of women all over the country. Historically isolated in the home, the club has given women a vehicle for political involvement.

"From Collective Buying to All Life"

The Seikatsu Club members are able to satisfy their buying needs through collective purchase. But urban residents need services as well as raw materials. Why leave the service industry up to big business? With our own substantial market, we realized that the club had the capability to expand into the service sector as well.

As of May 1987, we had 12 workers' collectives in Tokyo, 11 in Kanagawa, four in Saitama, 10 in Chiba and four in Hokkaido. Workers invest, work in and manage their own enterprises which include recycling, "bento," Japanese-style boxed lunches, and home helper businesses.

Collectives offer housewives an opportunity to work to their full potential. The labor of most Japanese women is wasted on unskilled part-time work. But through managing their own businesses, members not only reap job satisfaction, they are able to make a constructive contribution to their local communities.

The Seikatsu Club also runs a Mutual Benefit Fund, a service which goes beyond simply selling insurance as a product. Participants contribute 200 yen per month in exchange for monetary assistance in case of accident or illness. In addition, we provide psychological support to our members and offer them voluntary labors, if necessary. The not-for-profit fund is managed by a committee.

As the basic principles of the Seikatsu Club have been well received in Korea, we accepted Korean trainees twice in 1983, and have strengthened our relationship through several visits since then. In 1985, a coop was established in Seoul. But, because Korean law does not yet acknowledge the coop system, it is run as one of the businesses of a mutual credit association.

Organizational Structure

The club's basic organizational unit, a "han," is headed by a leader who is elected by group members for a one-year term. The leader of the "han" brings the group's views to branch meetings where he or she has the right to vote.

At present, the Seikatsu Club has 153,000 members, grouped into 25,000 hans who meet in 100 or so branches in ten prefectures throughout Japan. Composed of roughly 500-1000 members, each branch develops its own agenda and activities. The executive organization of each branch consists of 10-20 members.

"a committee of 10-20 members, 80 percent of whom are women are responsible for the management and operation of the coop."

The General Assembly, the highest decision making body in the coop, is held once a year when members' views on policy are heard through their group leaders. The Board of Directors, a committee of 10-20 members, 80 percent of whom are women, are elected during the General Assembly, and are responsible for the management and operation of the coop.

The club allows all members to participate in the decision making

---

What Is Money?

Alan AtKisson

A few weeks ago, prompted by the arrival of a new credit card into my life, I felt an urgent need to know the answer to the question, "What is money?" I was astonished to realize that I didn't know. I knew the usual definitions: money is a medium of exchange, a measure of value, and a store of wealth. But these phrases reveal nothing of the essential mystery of money. They describe what money *does* in our society, not what it *is*. So I started searching.

My dictionary just deepened the mystery. The word *money* comes from the old Latin word *monere*, which means "to admonish" or "to warn." The word was also a surname for Juno, the matriarch of the gods, in whose temple at Rome money was coined. This news wasn't very encouraging: it was early in my search, and I was already receiving warnings from the gods.

But I pressed on, dodging lightning bolts left and right, and posed the question to a couple of sagacious friends. Former astrophysicist Robert Gilman—who for the past dozen years has been pointing his telescope at environmental and cultural systems instead of star systems—noted that money is "a convenient way to lose a lot of information." When you buy a new shirt, you have no way of seeing the cotton fields, oil wells, plastics factories, and impoverished Asian laborers who process. Although the concept of democracy exists in theory in Japan, it is blurred by the bureaucracy of our political process. But in the Seikatsu Club, we are seeking to empower each and every member with a voice and a role in participatory politics.

Our full-time staff of 700 is responsible for duties carried out more efficiently if they are specialized, such as delivering goods, collecting group requests and settling accounts. They also assist members with committee work and in planning activities.

---

contributed to its production, because the money effectively hides all that.

That was a valuable insight, but not the answer I was looking for. So I consulted Joe Dominguez, a former Wall Street analyst who writes and teaches about personal economics. "Money is just life-energy," says Joe. We each have only so much life-time, and we seem to spend about a third of it *converting* it into money, usually through jobs. We spend another third of our lives *spending* the money, and another third tossing and turning in our sleep because we're *worried* about money.

I began to see that Joe's definition could have a revolutionary impact on one's attitude toward money and work—but I wanted something still deeper. When pressed, Joe told me a story about a remote Mexican village where, periodically, there was no money—not a single peso in the whole town. Under those conditions, Joe reported, people still invent money: "I'll give you three hours of my time for a couple of those fish," they might say.

I was puzzled. Why didn't they just *give* the fish, and the time, to each other? That's when it hit me: the dangerous truth about money. It's the *opposite* of a gift. A gift is an expression of love and trust and community. Money, therefore, is an expression of our distrust and fear, and our basic separation from each other. It's not a "measure of value." It's a measure of our lack of love.

They say that money is the root of all evil. But maybe that's backwards: maybe evil is the root of all money.

12

The Voluntary Green Tax

David Albert

Most products—even "green" ones—involve a certain amount of environmental degradation in their manufacture, consumption, distribution to market and disposal after use. These costs are borne by the air, the land, the water, other species and, eventually, us. But no accounting of these hidden costs is incorporated into the price of commodities, nor is there currently any way to charge a portion of the price of goods to ensure that the environment is restored after such economic activity occurs. Governments, although in a unique position to tax goods and services for this purpose, have been singularly unwilling to do so. On the contrary, they regard their business as doing the opposite: building yet more roads, for example, or providing tax incentives for further economic activity which, in turn, contributes to further environmental destruction.

In the absence of bioregional governments which might properly be expected to take such over-arching ecological issues to heart, a voluntary initiative of this kind has been startlingly successful. One of the originators of the idea, David Albert of New Society Publishers, explains how you, too, can implement interim green taxation until we get the kind of governments our bioregions are crying out for.

In the summer of 1988, after a long period of reflection, I presented a conundrum to the first national meeting of the "Socially Conscious Direct Mail Entrepreneurs' Network." Somewhat fearful of using the traditional language of economics, which for many often does little but obscure the obvious, I presented it in the form of an example:

New Society Publishers produces and distributes books which promote fundamental social change through nonviolent action. One of our books—*Thinking Like a Mountain: Towards a Council of All Beings*—is designed to help us remember that defense of the cnvironment is in reality a form of "self" defense. We'd like to sell tens of thousands of copies (and since then we have!), and we hope people will read them, too! People would have their consciousness raised and, of course, extra sales would help us increase our cashflow, hence allowing us to publish more books. None of the publishers individually would benefit financially for, as a worker-self-managed trusteeship business, our salaries are tied to our evolving concept of "right livelihood."

The problem is that the production and distribution of our books contributes to the environmental depletion that this book itself decries. While our books are printed on at least partially recycled paper, trees are cut down to manufacture them. Our advertising broadsheets are printed with recycled ink, but liquid industrial wastes are still produced in the process. The trucks which haul the newspapers to the recycling plants, the paper to the presses, and the finished books to customers burn petroleum products and pollute the air.

But the problem goes even deeper. One of the authors of *Thinking Like a Mountain*—John Seed, director of the Rainforest Information Centre in New South Wales, Australia—lectures around the world to promote a heightening of public consciousness about the seriousness of environmental threat. He donates all his speaking fees to the support of an indigenous rainforest project in Ecuador. Hundreds, even thousands of people travel scores of miles to hear him, burning up even more fossil fuels in the process. And, ironically, the more successful our book, and the more successful John's tours, the higher the environmental cost....

"the costs of restoring the environment to the state in which it existed before economic activity took place, are external to the exchange which happens in the marketplace and nowhere figured into the price of the product or service exchanged."

I'd like to believe that there is somewhere something like a "pure" exchange which doesn't involve these kinds of costs, but after some reflection one finds that these are rare indeed. The person who barters organically grown vegetables from her farm for a massage in town uses iron and steel tools industrially-forged using electricity produced by nuclear power or through coal-fired generation, with their own share of environmental costs, drives a vehicle mounted on rubber tires into town using fuels produced seven thousand miles away, and benefits from massage oils brought up by UPS trucks.

The point is that these costs or, more correctly, what the cost would be of restoring the environment to the state in which it existed before economic activity took place, are external to the exchange which happens in the marketplace and nowhere figured into the price of the product or service exchanged.

No Simple Solutions

There are no simple solutions to the conundrum. In theory, governments could tax economic activity to 1. Generally discourage economic activity; 2. Provide mass funds for environmental cleanup and restoration; and 3. Tax resources at their source in order to increasingly discourage their use as they approach depletion. They could also put the market itself under strict control. Theoretically, all of these ideas might work, but our experience of the possibility of such a government being empowered by its wise people to carry out these tasks, and the possibility of the government actually performing these tasks well is not likely to happen any time soon. (Parenthetically, if social awareness ever developed to the point where consensus for such necessary steps were achieved, and government had developed to the point where it could be counted on to implement the social consensus of its constituents, it might well be argued that we wouldn't need government as we now think of it all!) So meanwhile we need to look toward other possibilities.

We could decide, as many corporations ranging from Ben and Jerry's Ice Cream to Weyerhauser Paper to Mobil Oil(!) already have, to donate a portion of our profits to good purposes, including environmental restoration. Surely that's terrific as far as it goes, but the "charity" of benevolent capitalism, operating in a "free" market is no solution to the problem and, in fact, clouds matters still further. For companies that already engage in activities which cause damage to the environment (and virtually all do—it's just a matter of degree), the more damage they did and the higher the profits, the more money would go to restoration. But the restoration would never catch up with the damage! And of course there's no reason to believe that less profitable companies cause less environmental damage than more profitable ones. On the contrary: companies with smaller rates of profits or even losses are even more likely to skimp when it comes to environmental protection.

For us as a small business, the solutions are even more difficult to come by. We could raise our prices to provide funds for environmental restoration, but such an approach would most likely backfire. We are already a small business unable to take significant advantage of economies of scale. By placing ourselves at a "competitive disadvantage," sales of materials expressly meant to raise public consciousness would drop, lessening our capacity to serve a wider public, and cutting our margins still further.

The Green Tax

After taking account of all these considerations, we came up with the idea of a voluntary "Green Tax." The Green Tax is a convenient way for consumers to offset the environmental costs of the products we consume. We started to give our customers an opportunity to participate in the tax as part of their book order, by adding a line on our catalog order form, with a note of explanation as to what the "tax" is for. We suggested nine percent, though we must note that the actual environmental costs of all "externalities" accumulated over time—building and maintenance of roads, air and water pollution, environmental costs of power generation, etc.—might in some cases approach 100 percent of the purchase price of many commodities! We started to dispense the accumulated "Green Fund," using 50 percent of the funds generated for actual environmental restoration (tree planting, river and ocean cleanup, reinhabitation projects) and 50 percent for environmental education and direct action. We decided to use most of the restoration funds in our own bioregion, especially in the neighborhoods of our businesses, so that we can monitor their effectiveness, and take part in the projects themselves. We've used the other half of the funds nationally or even internationally where they will do the most good. The business absorbs all costs of distribution.

Among ourselves, we decided to have the workers at the company constitute the board for our "Green Fund." We knew that this might not be the most "efficient" way to dispense funds but, on the other hand, we thought that the consciousness-raising effect of thinking about these issues among our own staff would more than compensate. Since instituting our "Green Fund," we have given away some $10,000 to more than fifty groups and organizations such as:

- Ecology Action of Santa Cruz, aiding community-based recycling;
- Save Our Shores, working to preserve the biotic health and beauty of Central California coastal areas;
- Native Animal Rescue, for treating injured or orphaned wildlife and releasing them back into the environment;
- Philadelphia Urban Gardening, for developing youth projects in hydroponic gardening and garbage-recycling worm farms;
- The Nature Conservancy, for purchasing rare coastal plane forests in the Delaware Valley;
- Friends of Clark Park, for helping to revive an urban park en-

vironment in Philadelphia;

- The Tobar Donoso Project, for preservation of a large expanse of Ecuadorean rainforest and its indigenous culture;
- VICE (Volunteer Independent Cleanup Effort), endeavoring to clean up Alaskan beaches to state Department of Environmental Conservation standards after the Exxon oil spill in an ecologically low impact way which encourages community participation;
- The All Species Project, working to integrate ecology, cultural arts and community pageantry into the curriculum of public schools;
- The Rainforest Action Group, fighting to stop the building of a 500-megawatt geothermal unit threatening the last lowland tropical rainforest in Hawaii;
- Preserve Appalachian Wilderness, coordinating the transfer of private lands in northern New England to public wilderness preserve, and incorporating a sustainable economic plan;
- Kayapo Defense Fund, publicizing the struggles for survival of the Kayapo indigenous people of the Amazon rainforest in Brazil;
- Project Arunachala, reforesting the area surrounding a major temple shrine in south India;
- Forests Forever, working for a forest and wildlife protection initiative in California;
- Friends of the Ganges, cleaning up the Ganges River around the ancient city of Benares, India;
- The Mattole Restoration Council, protecting and enhancing salmon habitat in the Mattole region of California;
- The Save Georgia Strait Alliance, endeavoring to stop the environmental degradation of the Georgia Strait in British Columbia.

Growth in Campaign

With no advertising, solicitation, or coordination except a note in our catalog, the Green Tax idea seems to have caught on very quickly. Several dozen newsletters and magazines ran articles about it, and only eighteen months after we started, some one hundred plus businesses have instituted some version of the Green Tax. One business, TOPS LEARNING SYSTEMS in Canby, Oregon, which produces innovative science materials for classrooms, has gone so far as to add the Green Tax to invoices sent to school districts and has experienced a very high compliance rate.

Probably the most advanced manifestation of the Green Tax thus far has been the creation of the Finger Lakes Bioregional Green Fund in upstate New York. Started by Steve Siergirk of Acorn Designs, a producer of stationery and other products featuring environmental designs on recycled paper, the Fund has expanded to include dozens of businesses.

The Finger Lakes Bioregional Green Fund differs from most of the other efforts thus far because it is committed to raising consciousness among "walk-in customers." Among the members thus far are included seven restaurants, several gift shops, two print shops, a tire store, a general store, a video store, and a pet shop. Each of the stores, located in downtown Ithaca, display a "Green Fund" logo on their windows or doors, and has a rack with display materials at the check-out register. Clerks ask customers whether they would like to add a "green tax" to the amount of their purchase, and refer them to the printed materials (provided by the fund) if they have any questions about its operation. A Green Tax director has been hired to collect the funds monthly, to recruit new businesses, and to ensure that each business is properly equipped. A volunteer board made up of business members and representatives of the environmental community make decisions about the disbursement of funds. And, every month, the local newspaper has agreed to run a "Green Fund" column, talking about one of the member businesses and reporting on the disbursement of funds.

"by acknowledging our "environmental debt" as a business, we expect the maintenance of the Green Fund to be not only a consciousness-raiser for our customers, but for ourselves as well."

The Finger Lakes Bioregional Green Fund is an exciting new model in that it invites participation from all businesses, not simply those which, because of the nature of their products, carry a strong ecological message. It also allows for the creative use of community organizing skills, combined with a sound financial base, for the spread of ecological ideals, and for community education concerning the ecological needs of their particular bioregion, without losing sight of the global challenge that the environmental crisis represents.

We are aware that the Green Tax is not an "answer" to environmental problems. While we are proud of the contributions we and our customers are making to restoring the environment, we would be naive to think that this could ever approach the level truly needed to make a long-term difference. What we *do* hope the Green Tax will do, if it spreads widely enough, is provide a simple way to begin dialogue among larger segments of the population at the grassroots level so that more lasting answers can be found. And by acknowledging our "environmental debt" as a business, we expect the maintenance of the Green Fund to be not only a consciousness-raiser for our customers, but for ourselves as well.

(For more information about the Finger Lakes Green Fund, and about instituting the Green Tax in your business or community, contact Finger Lakes Green Fund, P.O. Box 6578, Ithaca, NY 14851; telephone: (607) 387-3424.)

13

Deli Dollars, Trash Cash and Local Loans

An interview with Susan Witt

In the town of Great Barrington, Massachusetts, the historically inde-pendent-minded inhabitants still enjoy participating in schemes that maintain their autonomy from the centralized powers-that-be. This provides fertile ground for economic initiatives of an unconventional kind which free up peoples' creativity, build community trust and solidarity, and help keep regional wealth in the regions, where it belongs.

Susan Witt works with the E.F. Schumacher Society in Great Barrington and is an administrator of SHARE—the Self Help Association for a Regional Economy—in that town. In this interview with The New Catalyst, she explains how a genuine greening of local financial institutions can be encouraged in your local town—a step along the path to regions regaining control of their economies.

The New Catalyst: *Can you give us an idea of how SHARE began and what exactly you are doing with it?*

Susan Witt: The SHARE Program is a small loan collateralization program that's been active for about seven years. People in the area have come to know us as being interested in financing small businesses. So when our local Deli—a restaurant well-loved by many people in town, with community bulletin boards there, young college students, construc-tion workers, the vacation home people, all meeting there and having their meals—when news came that the Deli had to move its location because its lease was running out, and the bank had turned down their application for a loan, there was community support to help do some-thing about it. Frank, the owner of the Deli came to SHARE and we suggested that he issue his own currency—Deli Dollars—and sell them to his customers in order to raise the capital he needed to renovate the new spot.

TNC: *Was he unable to go to the bank?*

Susan Witt: He tried the bank and, although all the bankers ate at the Deli on a regular basis, nonetheless his figures didn't work out on paper, in part because he kept his prices low and just worked long hours, so they didn't compute. But in the community mind they *did* compute because everyone knew that Frank wouldn't go bad on the loan, he'd just work harder.

TNC: *So how did his Deli Dollars work?*

Susan Witt: Well, what he did was to presell meals to his customers. He sold a ten-dollar Deli Dollar for nine dollars in October to be redeemable at the new business, once it was renovated, for ten dollars worth of sandwiches. However, to ensure that all the Deli Dollars didn't come in the first month, they were dated over a ten month period. So some came due in February, some March, some April. There was just terrific, enthusiastic response. The contractors found it was a great Christmas present for their crew members—they gave away a whole slew of them. One even showed up in the collection plate for the local Congregational Church because the Minister was known to have regular breakfasts at the Deli.

TNC: *How much money did Frank raise this way?*

Susan Witt: In one month, he raised $5,000. To Frank that was a very low interest loan because he would be paying back not in ten dollars of federal money but in the contents of sprout and cheese sandwiches. So he wouldn't have to repay any dollar value. The customers liked being part of helping Frank move. They felt, in a way, that they were beating the system because they were helping to find a way of keeping the Deli in town through their own efforts. Actually, some people have told us that they bought Deli Dollars and they didn't even go there to eat. They just wanted to be a part of the whole concept!

TNC: *I believe you've also initiated another program that helps farmers go through slack winter times?*

Susan Witt: This group grew directly out of the Deli Dollar program and it's the way things happen in a small town. One of the people working at the Deli was Jan whose parents ran a farm stand. So, of course, she went home and told them all about the Deli Dollars. Now Martha and Dan got the idea that if there could be Deli Dollars, why couldn't there be "Greensback." During the winter months, they have to keep their greenhouses going with high oil bills, yet they're not selling their own produce. They're growing the plants for the spring and summer! They thought maybe their customers would help them by pre-buying their plants, giving them federal dollars in the winter and getting "greens back" in the summer. It worked out a little differently, though. At the same time another farm stand—owned by a family that was very well-loved in the community—experienced a devastating fire.They got a lot of help with rebuilding, and so on. One of the SHARE members asked why we didn't do a Corn Crib Dollar?

"Instead of a Federal Reserve note it was a Berkshire Farm Note, and instead of "In God We Trust," it said, "In Farms We Trust," and instead of the head of George Washington, it had the head of a cabbage!"

These two proposals came to us at once and we suggested that they work together. Out of this grew Berkshire Farm Preserve Notes. Instead of a Federal Reserve note it was a Berkshire Farm Note, and instead of "In God We Trust," it said, "In Farms We Trust," and instead of the head of George Washington, it had the head of a cabbage! The interesting thing about this is that they were sold at either location and redeemable at either location. So it was pushing more towards a currency than just the in and out of the Deli Dollar. Again, they were dated so that they would come in during June, July, August, September and October.

TNC: *Because they were redeemable at both locations, was there some system in place to account for an imbalance?*

Susan Witt: Correct. That was a major role that SHARE played. Essentially it was SHARE that issued the notes to the farmers, and the farmers were under obligation to return the same number of redeemed notes back. If they didn't, they'd have to pay for the ones that were not returned to them. If they had extras, SHARE was under obligation to purchase those back at the sale price. So, SHARE became a clearinghouse to equalize the redemption, rather than the farmers working it out. They each raised about $3,500. Next year we'd like to include other farm stands, and also include the restaurants that buy from those farm stands. So it would be a food-related dollar, affirming to consumers that the restaurants using Berkshire Farm Notes are also buying locally—using fresh food and supporting the local economy.

TNC: *It sounds like a unique set of experiments working very successfully. Could this just happen anywhere, or have you been laying the ground work?*

Susan Witt: It's been about seven years since we started the SHARE program. We just began with simple local collateralization projects where our members make deposits at the local bank and are issued passbook savings accounts and agree that those accounts can be used to collateralize small loans, meeting social, environmental, as well as financial, criteria. These are loans that otherwise wouldn't have been funded by banks—women without credit history doing work in their own homes, or organic farms with products unfamiliar to the banking industry. For instance, goat cheese was one of our loans.

TNC: *Can you give us a couple of examples of who SHARE has financed?*

Susan Witt: One was Bonnie. She had a knitting machine in her home. She was buying four skeins of yarn at a time, knitting garments for children, selling them, and buying another four skeins, knitting, selling. Of course this is not the most efficient way to do things, but she didn't have the credit with the yarn suppliers to buy bulk supplies. So she came to SHARE and borrowed $500. She put in a bulk order, got her credit, and didn't need us again for that.

She came back later and said her orders were increasing. She needed a new knitting machine that does a different type of stitch so she could have more variety in the garments. She borrowed $1,500 and, again, all we did was collateralize the loan that goes through the local bank. She repaid that loan, came back and said that she had so many customers that she needed *another* knitting machine to have someone working with her. We said, "You don't need us any more, Bonnie. You should just go to the bank and borrow it." She said, "Well, not me. A bank isn't interested in me. I've never had credit at a bank." We told her that she'd had two loans through a bank, each repaid, and that she now had a credit history with those banks. A week later Bonnie called, very enthusiastic: she'd been given a loan. So, SHARE is also about getting people off of needing to borrow from SHARE.

TNC: *Are most of the projects that you fund small, cottage industries?*

Susan Witt: Yes. Our first loan was to Sue who had her own dairy goat herd and was creating a very fine quality goat cheese that she was selling from her back door. Sue had built the barn from wood that she'd cleared from her own land, had bartered what equipment she had, and had had no need to borrow, had no credit history. She'd gone to the bank with the proposal to fund equipment to build a state-approved milking room because she wanted to expand and sell her product to stores and restaurants but needed a licenced milking room in order to do that. She couldn't barter for the Anderson windows, the cement floors, the stainless steel tanks. It had to be cash.

She went to the bank and they said, "What's goat cheese? It's an unfamiliar product. Doesn't it smell? Who would really want it?" She came to SHARE and members took her cheese and tested it. They went to two different stores in town and asked them if they would buy the cheese and, if so, how much would they pay for it? By testing the market, they found there was one and made the loan.

SHARE members are kept informed about what products they're investing in. We talk about bringing "visibility" to our investments. Instead of just earning interest, which might be nuclear power plants or investments in South Africa, our investors know what their money is doing tonight. It's invested in Sue's goat farm. It's invested in Jim's draft horse team. It's invested in Bonnie's knitting machine. Our transactions with money become visible and that abstractness which hides the reality of currency circulation is made visible again.

TNC: *What concrete advantages does that have?*

Susan Witt: Well, then our loans become more than just an effect in the economy. Our depositers, when they learn where their money is going, go down to Sue's farm to take a look at what she's been doing. The little goats come up and nibble at their keys in their pockets. They're so cute that, the next time, they bring down their grandchildren to see them. The following week they come and get a big supply of cheese for a party they're going to give. Gradually, in this way, the loans that they've made begin to work into their social and cultural life. *The* goat cheese becomes *their* goat cheese, becomes identified with them, with their friends, with their way of life, with their habits. It takes on a different nature just in their house.

TNC: *So what starts out to be a simple financial arrangement turns out to be cultural solidarity.*

Susan Witt: That's the true test of these alternative economic projects. Unless they begin to penetrate into the social and cultural life, you don't have something that's quite working yet. You begin with the new economic form but you expect it to weave a web deep into other aspects of life, and knit it together.

TNC: *Can you tell us the mechanics of how SHARE works?*

Susan Witt: SHARE is organized as a simple, not-for-profit corporation. Anyone who is a resident of Berkshire region can become a member by simply walking into our local, participating bank. We did some hunting to find the right bank. We looked for a locally owned bank which had a good track record of investment in the community. You just walk into the bank and open a 90-day notice passbook savings account which is written as a joint account with SHARE. SHARE has already pre-signed all of its part of the documents and left them at the bank. So the potential SHARE member comes in, opens an account, and the passbook is kept at the bank for the SHARE representative to come in and get. In opening the account, the SHARE member agrees that that passbook can be used to collateralize loans which meet the criteria that SHARE outlines.

SHARE has a very simple overhead, because, even though some use rights have been given to SHARE, these accounts are solely and individually owned by the depositors, including the interest accumulated. Our SHARE accounts pay six percent interest. When a loan collateralization has been approved the SHARE coordinator—who may be working out of a file drawer, a post office box and a telephone number anywhere—takes out the passbooks, walks down to the bank and puts them up as collateral for the loan: enough books to cover the loan. We have a $3,000 limit. Other programs that have used the SHARE model have gone as high as $30,000. We're choosing to serve the small cottage-industry needs, but other regions might identify a different need.

"We're looking to help create the monetary and the financing systems that will keep that wealth flowing within that region. Connecting local investors with local projects, creating a one-to-one tie, through the SHARE lending program is one way of doing that."

TNC: *So, the banks are happy because they are gaining more business...*

Susan Witt: In fact what we have found in working with groups that have started SHARE programs in other areas is that the banks were eager to have the SHARE program in their bank because it helped them with their Community Reinvestment Act requirements. Under U.S. federal law, banks need to reinvest a certain amount of their deposits in the local community and must report to their community how they've met this obligation. The local loans that SHARE makes is helping them contribute to that obligation. The bank becomes visible as being community-spirited. We've had numbers of people just transfer their whole accounts to our SHARE participating bank because they feel they should support those institutions working with the community.

TNC: *How does this differ from a system such as LETS, or other barter systems?*

Susan Witt: The SHARE program is just a simple lending program, dealing with federal dollars, rather than with a created exchange system. With SHARE, including the kinds of experiments with currencies—Deli Dollars and Berkshire Farm Preserve Notes—our objective is to make only productive loans. In other words, loans that will increase the ability of the borrower to do more production. For example, Bonnie's knitting allowing Bonnie's hands to be more productive. So it's the *means of production* that we're financing, instead of an exchange of services. It has a different net effect in the economics of that community.

TNC: *Is this part of some grander strategy that you have in mind? How do you see this contributing to the regional economy?*

Susan Witt: Basically, we're looking to find the way in which wealth generated in the region can be kept in the region. Our local banks which did a very good job of that in the past have now been bought up by larger and larger holding companies. So the deposits, the earnings generated in rural regions and inner cities, become like the wealth generated in Third World areas: it tends to all flow out into a few central, international, urban centers. So, we're looking to find a way to help create the kinds of institutions that will encourage stronger, independent regions. We're looking to help create the monetary and the financing systems that will keep that wealth flowing within that region. Connecting local investors with local projects, creating a one-to-one tie, through the SHARE lending program is one way of doing that. Ties are built deeply through these connections. In fact, we find that the lenders become the best insurers of the success of the small businesses because they're then buying their products on a regular basis, chatting about it, and further insuring the success of those small businesses. Therefore, they're generating more jobs in that area, jobs that aren't polluting—"green jobs," if you will. We figure that just our 17 small loans through the SHARE program have generated three times as many permanent jobs in our area: that's a very low cost, job generating program.

TNC: *Do you see this as part of a more widely available regional currency?*

Susan Witt: Yes. That is ultimately the way that communities can regain independence and begin to unplug from the federal system: to take back their rights to generate their own regional currencies. As our area of Great Barrington gets used to exchanging Berkshire Farm Preserve Notes and Deli Dollars, we hope it will be the beginning of a true, independent, regional currency that's broadly circulated. We have been looking at various potential backings for that currency. We'd like it to be commodity-backed by some local product. In the past, baskets of farm goods have been used in the history of American development. Meanwhile, these projects keep walking through the door and we might have found one in "Trash Cash."

TNC: *Tell us about that.*

Susan Witt: This is good fun, but still only an idea. Rachel Fletcher, a board member in our community, took on the major task of helping to introduce recycling to individuals in the town of Great Barrington. She had a great time doing it. Rachel and the town would now like to take on recycling for businesses but needs a major investment of some $20,000 for the facilities at the town dump. Rachel went to the town fathers who said they had other priorities... As she was paying for her bill at the farmstand with her Berkshire Farm Preserve Notes, she thought why not "Trash Cash?" The town could sell to businesses a two to three year amount of Trash Cash.

Bioregional Economics

The E.F. Schumacher Society

Fritz Schumacher argued that from a truly economic point of view, the most rational way to produce is "from local resources, for local needs." Jane Jacobs re-emphasizes Fritz's point through her analysis of a healthy region as one creating "import replacing" industries on a continuing basis. A fully developed regional economy, producing for its own needs, is only possible, however, when control of resources and financing lies within the region itself. At present, ownership of land, natural resources and industry, and determination of conditions for receiving credit, have become increasingly centralized at the national level. As a result, all but a few large urban areas find that major control of their economic resources is foreign to the area.

This situation calls for a reorganization of economic institutions so that they are responsive to regional needs and conditions. These new economic structures will, by their very form, decentralize control of land, natural resources, industry and financing in an equitable manner among the people living in an area, so creating the infrastructure to facilitate full local production for local needs.

These considerations constitute the economic rationale for the development of Community Land Trusts, worker-owned and managed businesses, non-profit locally-controlled banks and regional currencies. Regional economies cannot be expected to flourish until all of these new, broadly democratic forms are implemented within each region, and the old centralized forms are in decline.

"Regional economies cannot be expected to flourish until all of these new, broadly democratic forms are implemented within each region, and the old centralized forms are in decline."

Of these new institutions perhaps the least understood will be that of regional currencies, because we have all become so accustomed to assuming that national currencies are the norm and preferable. In her book, *Cities and the Wealth of Nations*, (Random House, 1984) Jane Jacobs illustrates "how national currencies stifle the economies of regions."

TNC: *Dumping fees ahead of time?*

Susan Witt: Exactly. A business could calculate how much it pays in hauler's fees for taking away its garbage for a two to three year period, and pre-purchase that in Trash Cash from the town. The town would

---

She views the economy of a region as a living entity in the process of expanding and contracting. She understands the role of a regional currency as the appropriate regulator of this ebbing, flowing life. If a region does not produce enough of its own goods, relying heavily on imports, its currency is devalued. As a result, import costs increase, discouraging trade. At the same time, because the currency is less in demand, interest rates will decrease, thereby encouraging local borrowing for the production of "import replacing" goods. Conversely, if the region is adequately supplying its own needs, then its currency "hardens," that is, holds its real value relative to other currencies. As a result, imports are cheaper, encouraging trade, and interest rates higher.

"Currencies are powerful carriers of feedback information, then, and potent triggers of adjustments, but on their own terms. A national currency registers, above all, consolidated information on a nation's international trade," says Jacobs. But what information is then returned to the individual regions? "Imagine," Jacobs suggests, "a group of people who are all properly equipped with diaphragms and lungs but who share among them only one brainstem breathing center. In this goofy arrangement, the breathing center would receive consolidated feedback on the carbon dioxide level of the whole group and would be unable to discriminate among the individuals producing it. Everybody's diaphragm would be triggered to contract at the same time. But suppose some of those people were sleeping while others were playing tennis? Suppose some were reading about feedback controls while others were chopping wood?" Should the Industrial Great Lakes Region or the Farmbelt States, both in a condition of severe economic depression, adjust their local economies in the same manner as the thriving Sunbelt or the booming Silicon Valley of the west coast? Can small businesses in rural areas compete with international corporations and the federal government for access to national currency, especially when interest rates are kept artificially high by the federal government's policy of carrying a huge debt with seemingly no intention of repaying that debt?

The dependency on national currencies actually deprives regions of a very useful self-regulating tool and results in the paradoxical creation of stagnant economic pockets in a seemingly prosperous nation. Jane Jacobs' book is a stunning argument for independent currencies.

then have raised its $20,000 interest-free to build the recycling station. As the businesses get their bill from the haulers, they pay with Trash Cash. The haulers would then pay the dumping fees in Trash Cash. So it would circulate back. Once you have the town involved like that, maybe the town could pay a percentage of the wages to town employees in Trash Cash, who would use it at the local stores who have hauling fees, who would then even pay their town property taxes in Trash Cash. Once the town accepted Trash Cash, or any local currency, for property taxes, the potential for broad-based circulation would be enormous. It would mean that that Trash Cash would only circulate in the Great Barrington area. If someone had Trash Cash in their pocket, they couldn't shop through the L.L. Bean Catalogue. A rural area does a lot of shopping through catalogues, and that, too, takes money out of the area. It's a major problem we don't think about because catalogue-shopping seems convenient. But it's important to go downtown, using those local shops—Trash Cash will get you there!

14

Community Supported Agriculture: A Grassroots Food System

Alyssa Lovell

Alienation from the land and from our source of food are key characteristics of the modern malaise we call western civilization. Regarded as a mere commodity rather than the very stuff of life, food has been produced by steadily fewer and fewer people in the West in recent years. Where it is now not controlled by giant corporations, the risk and responsibility of agriculture is borne inequitably by individual farmers. Community Supported Agriculture aims to change all that, to finance the growing of food locally, thereby socializing the whole endeavor as well as restoring peoples' relationships to both land and food supply. Alyssa Lovell, from Vermont, reports on this initiative that holds great potential.

Do you know where your food comes from? Are you frustrated with the lack of information available about the food that we eat? Are you sickened and dismayed at the inevitable hidden costs of every bite that we put in our mouths? Do you wonder why farmers, who grow the food we all need, should be the sole bearers of the inherent economic and social risks of farming?

It's not easy to get a hold of socially responsible food these days, when our purchases at most grocery stores are actually votes for an infinitely complex world food system. This system not only makes us ignorant about the origins of our food but is also stigmatized by the exploitation of the agricultural worker of developing countries, and by the contamination of groundwater and air.

Now, for Central Vermonters and for folks in at least thirty other areas of the United States, and at least forty-five areas in Western Europe and Japan, there exists an option to be a part of a solution to the food system dilemma. A Community Supported Agriculture (CSA) project, starting at the Snow Baker Farm in Marshfield is helping local residents to start changing the way we participate in the agricultural system.

The Snow Baker CSA project is going to be community supported from the very bottom up. All major decisions about the project, including those about the budget and payment policy, varieties and amounts of crops to be grown, and the work policy will be made by a core group of both "harvest-sharers" and non-harvest sharers who have a particular interest in the project. Anyone who is involved with the project in some way is encouraged to attend several of the core group meetings, in order to become a voting member. As Lori Baker states, "This farm is their farm... The more the merrier!"

One of the issues that the Farm is currently working on is the definition of Community Supported Agriculture. According to Les Snow, "There is a great variation in the projects, but always the same basic concept, which is the provision of security for the farmer and the buyers." At the Brookfield Farm in South Amherst, Massachussetts, new members were attracted largely by word of mouth. There, members agreed among themselves to feed children of members free of charge, at least during the first couple of years.

The project anticipates being able to provide fifty "sharers" (a "sharer" is equal to two people) with eight to ten pounds of organic vegetables for a full forty-week season. For the approximately twenty-five week winter season, the farm plans to provide twenty additional harvest-shares. Each harvest-share costs $369.00, which includes funds ten percent over the actual cost of the vegetables to cover the risk factor during the first year. The price, multiplied by fifty harvest-shares, should support two full-time workers. The core group is currently applying for grants from businesses in hopes of lowering the project's start-up cost.

CSA is perhaps catching on more quickly than was expected in Vermont. However, considering the public's increasing awareness about food systems and the continuing struggle of organic growers' co-ops, CSA makes sense as a practical alternative. An example of a recent event which opens our eyes to the necessity of shared-risk farming is the Vermont Northern Growers' (VNG) loss of bushels of stored vegetables to the cold. The economic burden of the loss is borne by too few, compared to the number of mouths that the vegetables would have fed. Louis Pulver, one of the VNG growers, says that the co-op is now looking ahead for new ways to work within its established organization. He is enthusiatic about CSA, pointing out that up-front payment is an important aspect, because "banks gouge farmers the hardest in the spring, when expenses are high."

The "Share The Harvest" Concept

Community Supported Agriculture was founded in this country by a group of farmers and concerned people in South Egremont, Massachussets, in the mid-1980s. There, Robyn Van En had been farming for two years independently and was feeling the burden of her capitalization risk and workload, despite a committed consumer group. The answer to her problems came when she met with Jan Vander Tuin, John Root, and Hugh Radcliffe to plan a first season of the "share the harvest" concept, for the summer of 1985. Jan, in turn, had brought the concept of CSA back with him from Switzerland, where he had been farming with such a project since 1982.

The tradition of CSA goes back for over twenty-five years in Western Europe and Japan. The Seikatsu Club Consumers Cooperative (SCCC), founded in the Tokyo area in 1965 by 200 women interested in finding cheaper milk prices, has evolved to a 150,000 member-family buying cooperative, with social, economic, and political purposes (see Chapter 12). In 1989, the SCCC was awarded The Right Livelihood Honorary Award by the School of Peace Studies at the University of Bradford in the United Kingdom: "The Jury honours in Seikatsu the most successful model of production and consumption in the industrialized world, aiming to change society by promoting self-managed and less wasteful lifestyles."

Trauger Groh, a CSA grower in southern Hew Hampshire, explained some of his views about CSA's place in the larger society during a recent telephone interview. When asked about the way in which a CSA could be permanently built into the structure of a community, he explained that "the special thing about CSA is that it is based on the constantly reviewed initiative of people... No legal form can really be used to perpetuate it." The policy of a CSA will never be permanently established because it is the direct result of people's ongoing involvement. However, Trauger emphasized that CSA does have a type of permanence as a goal. He calls it "soil-based permanent fertility." The objectives of this goal include producing "an ever larger diversity (within the farm ecosystem), adapted to the needs of the local population...(eventually) using no substances or energy from outside the farm... This is part of an important economic goal."

Trauger sees that the family farm is no longer a sustainable institution. It puts too much of a burden on one family, and is, he says, "especially difficult on women," because they want to farm as well as raise the family [sic]. Jan Vander Tuin says that farming should always be done in a group, as is done at his 75-family CSA in Temple and Wilton, New Hampshire. CSA supports his view that group farming is the best farming.

The economic and social implications of CSA are exciting for Vermont, where a 200-year agricultural tradition is in dire need of revitalization. Vermont currently imports over seventy percent of its food, and much of the agricultural activity here, namely dairly, is oriented toward export markets. The already glutted dairy market, which can't even support its producers with living wages, is being pressured further by the introduction of bovine somatotropin (BST), a growth hormone which induces increased milk production in the average dairy cow. This and other events are continuations of the anti-agricultural trend which began in this country after World War II, initiated by governmental policies such as parity and by organizations such as the Committee for Economic Development. The trend has been away from small-scale, local farms and toward conglomerate agribusiness, monocroppings, and an export-oriented economy.

"CSA is a grassroots action which allows people to reclaim their rights to appropriate and healthy agriculture and an actual relationship with the land."

In Vermont, there is still a high percentage of small, local producers who market locally, but their markets are not always accessible to the average consumer. The Vermont Department of Agriculture promotes these producers through pamphlets and agricultural fairs, but does not go so far as to establish an actual regional market. A regional market, such as the kind created by CSA, has several advantages over a national or international market, for both the producer, the consumer, and the environment. First, although some diversity is sacrificed (you won't be provided with Dole pineapples, for instance), it provides fresh, often organic (and, in the case of some CSA's, biodynamic) produce, using much less fossil fuel and human energy than is used in the dominant American food system. It eliminates the extraneous packaging and repackaging which, though creating jobs, creates waste for the consumer to deal with. The vertical integration which tends to accompany regional markets provides producers with a more stable economic situation, one less influenced by the fluctuations of the traditional export/market economy. A price comparison done at the Brookfield Farm, a CSA in

Amherst, Massachusetts, showed a fifty percent reduction in prices compared with equivalent produce in a retail store. CSA can also protect farmers from the trials of having to obtain loans and subsidies from the government, the route that post-war credit farming took and failed under.

CSA is a grassroots action which allows people to reclaim their rights to appropriate and healthy agriculture and an actual relationship with the land. There are several ways in which people, even those who live in an urban or suburban environment, can organize to form a CSA project. CSA can create a new social structure for a community, providing an arena for people to gather and work together in rhythm with the seasons and cycles of the farm, cleaning, storing, canning, drying and cooking their produce.

It seems that CSA can be a perfect way for people who do not have the resources to be farmers themselves to participate in the production of their own food. It is a way for people to compensate for the country's sagging agricultural system, to instill support for local agriculture into their communities, and to overcome the poisoned environmental circumstances which mainstream agriculture has created for everyone.

15

Amish Economics

Gene Logsdon

The crisis in agriculture has resulted not only from the ownership of farms and the internationalization of farm markets, but also from the pressure of new technologies. As farm bankruptcies multiply throughout the "developed" world—through increased payments for pesticides, inorganic fertilizers, interest on loans to buy big machinery, and so on—agriculture is being left to agribusiness. By sticking to "outmoded" traditions, however, the Amish provide a living example of an alternative in action. At the same time, as Gene Logsdon reports, the continuing success of the Amish in farming is very much tied to their all-embracing cultural alternative that shuns fossil-fuelled machinery and centralized electric power. The Amish, in short, have been doing deep green business for decades!

Amish farmers are still making money in these hard times despite (or rather because of) their supposedly outmoded, horse-farming ways. If they do get into financial jeopardy, it is most often from listening to the promises of modern agribusiness instead of traditional wisdom. The Amish continue to farm profitably not only with an innocent disregard for get-big-or-get-out modern technology, but without participating in direct government subsidies other than those built into market prices, which they can't avoid.

Barn-raising in a Single Day

I first learned about the startlingly effective economy of Amish life when I was invited to a barn raising near Wooster, Ohio. A tornado had levelled four barns and acres of prime Amish timber. In just three weeks, the downed trees were sawed into girders, posts and beams and the four barns rebuilt and filled with livestock donated by neighbours to replace those killed by the storm. Three weeks! Nor were the barns the usual modern, one-storey metal boxes hung on poles. They were huge buildings, three and four storeys high, post-and-beam framed, and held together with hand-hewn mortises and tenons. I watched the raising of the last barn in open-mouthed awe. Some 400 Amish men and boys, acting and reacting like a hive of bees in absolute harmony of cooperation, started at sunrise with only a foundation and floor and by noon had the huge edifice far enough along that you could put hay in it.

A contractor who was watching said it would have taken him and a beefed-up crew all summer to build the barn if, indeed, he could find anyone skilled enough at mortising to do it. He estimated the cost at $100,000. I asked the Amish farmer how much cash he would have in the barn. "About $30,000," he said. And some of that paid out by the Amish church's own insurance arrangements. "We give each other our labour," he explained. "We look forward to raisings. There are so many helping, no one has to work too hard. We get in a good visit."

Not long afterwards, I gave a speech to an organization of farmers concerned with alternative methods of agriculture in which I commiserated at length with the financially depressed farmers. When my talk was over, two Amish men approached me, offering mild criticism. "We have finished one of our most financially successful years," one of them said. "It is only those farmers who have ignored common sense and tradition who are in trouble." What made his remarks more significant is that he went on to explain that he belonged to a group of Amish that had, as an experiment, temporarily allowed its members to use tractors in the field. He also was making payments on land that he had recently purchased. In other words, he was staring at the same economic gun that's pointed at English farmers and he was coming out ahead. "But," he said, "I'm going back to horses. They're more profitable."

When I helped a neighbor haul hay, I received another lesson in Amish economics. If they need to buy extra feed for their livestock, they almost always choose to buy hay and raise the grain rather than vice versa. The price of the hay is partially regained as manure after passing through the livestock, allowing them to cut down on the amount of fertilizer they need to buy. The greater mass of hay generates a greater mass of manure, adding organic matter to the soil. That is valuable beyond computer calculation. Grain farmers in my area who sold their straw and hay to the Amish were trading their soil fertility for cash of flitting value.

Umbilical Cords to the Dangerous Outside World

Housing is another good example of Amish economy. First of all, the Amish home doubles as an Amish church. How many millions of dollars this saves the Amish would be hard to calculate. Secondly, the Amish home doubles as the Amish retirement village and nursing home, thereby saving incalculably more millions of dollars, not to mention the self-respect of the elderly. The Amish do not pay Social Security, nor do they accept it. They know and practice a much better security that requires neither pension nor lifelong savings.

There is an old Amish quiltmaker who lives near Pffeifer's Station, a crossroads store and village I often frequent. Her bedroom is just big enough for a bed and quilting frame; her kitchen is equally tiny. The boys of the family keep the walkway stacked with firewood for her stove. She has her own little garden. Children play on her doorstep.

She has her privacy but is surrounded by living love, not the dutiful professionalism of the old folks' home. And she still earns her way. Quilt buyers come, adding to her waiting list more quilts than her fingers, now slowed by arthritis, can ever catch up with. I love that scene. She still lives in the real world. If she were not Amish, she would have languished in some nursing home and no doubt be dead by now—from sheer boredom if nothing else.

"It is in agriculture that the Amish raise economy to a high art.... The Amish farmers all agreed that, with 20 cows, a farmer could gross $50,000 in a good-weather year"

There are no telephones in the homes, but the Amish use the telephone booths that dot the roadsides. An Amishman views a telephone wire in the home, like an electric line, as an umbilical cord tying them to dangerous worldly influences. You will not talk so long or often at a pay booth down the road.

Whatever one's views of such fence-straddling religious convictions, they obviously reveal tremendous economizing. In a 1972 study of Illinois Old Order Amish conducted by the Center for the Biology of Natural Systems at Washington University in St. Louis, Amish housewives said they spent $10 to $15 a week on food and non-food groceries. They reported household living expenses from $1379 for a small young family up to $4,700 for a large, better-financed one. My own Amish informants thought that today, that figure might top out at $8000 for a large family, including transportation by buggy and occasionally renting a car or riding a bus. A horse and new buggy cost about $2,000 and last a good bit longer than a $12,000 car.

Medical costs are the only expenses the Amish cannot control by their sub-economy. Religion forbids education beyond the early teens, so they cannot generate their own doctors and medical facilities, and must pay the same ridiculous rates as the rest of us.

Another surprising element in the Amish economy is the busy social life they lead within a day's ride by buggy or bicycle. We could scarcely schedule a softball game because there was always a wedding, a raising, a sale, a quilting, or church and school doings to attend! I can assure the world that the Amish have just as much fun as anyone, at far less than the cost of weekends made for Michelob.

A Livelihood on Twenty Cows

It is in agriculture that the Amish raise economy to a high art. After the ball-games, when talk got around to the hard times in farming today, the Amish said a good farmer could still make a good living with a herd of 20 to 25 cows. The Amish farmers all agreed that, with 20 cows, a farmer could gross $50,000 in a good- weather year, of which "about half" would be net after paying farm expenses including taxes and interest on land debt, if any. Deducting $8,000 for family living expenses still leaves a nice nest egg for emergencies, bad years, and savings to help offspring get started in farming.

The most amazing part of the Amish economy to me is that, contrary to notions cherished by old farm magazine editors who escaped grim childhoods on 1930s farms for softer lives behind desks, the Amish do not work as hard, physically, as I did when my father and I were milking 100 cows with all the modern conveniences in the 1960s.

English farmers like to make fun of the Amish for their hair- splitting ways with technology—allowing tractors or engines for stationary power tools but not in the fields. But in addition to keeping the Amish way of life intact, such compromises bring tremendous economy to their farming while lightening the workload. A motor-powered baler or corn harvester, pulled by horses ahead of a forecart, may seem ridiculous to a modern agribusinessman, but it saves thousands of dollars over buying tractors for this work. The reasons tractors aren't allowed in the fields is that they would then tempt an Amishman to expand acreage, going into steep debt to do so, and in the process drive other Amish off the land—which is exactly why and how American agriculture got into the trouble engulfing it today.

To satisfy religious restrictions, the Amish have developed many other ingenious ideas to use modern technology in economizing ways. Other farmers should be studying, not belittling, them. When Grade A milk regulations forced electric cooling tanks on dairymen, the Amish adopted diesel motors to generate their own electricity for the milk room, cooler and milk machines. They say it's cheaper than buying electricity and keeps them secure from power outages.

Where Amish are active, countryside and town are full of bustling shops and small businesses, neat homes, solid schools and churches, and scores of roadside stands and cheese factories. East central Ohio even has a small woollen mill, one of the few remaining in the country. Compare this region with the decaying towns and empty farmsteads of the land dominated by large-scale agribusiness. The Amish economy spills out to affect the whole local economy. Some farmers, like Lancie Cleppinger near Mount Vernon, have the great good sense to farm like the Amish even though they don't live like them. They enjoy profits too. When discussing the problems agribusiness farmers have brought on themselves, Cleppinger just shook his head and repeated, "What in the world are they thinking?"

16

Wildwood:
A Forest For The Future

Ruth Loomis with Merv Wilkinson

The task of making the major resource extraction industries sustainable over the long-term is truly a challenge for those who would promote green business. The answer, in part, lies in the scale of operation: the clearcutting of vast acreages is only thinkable in the context of a mass international market, governed by multinational corporations with no eye on the long-term future. Equally important are the understandings and attitudes brought to bear upon the forest ecosystem and humanity's relationship to it. Mass-scale industrial techniques preclude our really knowing and caring for what is looked upon as just a "resource." Human-scale forestry is not only more deeply satisfying for those who work in the woods, it also ensures that forest ecosystems remain intact into the future. "Old- timer" Merv Wilkinson, from British Columbia, collaborated with writer, Ruth Loomis, to describe how green foresty can be done.

My 136 acre tree farm, "Wildwood," at Yellowpoint near Ladysmith on Vancouver Island, is a sustained-yield, selectively logged tract of timber that has been producing forest products since 1945, and will continue to do so indefinitely. Here, there is still a forest and it is growing faster than I log it. I make a good living without destroying the forest. I work with nature. I harvest trees periodically for specialized products and on a regular basis for lumber, enjoying the forest, and its tranquility where all the living organisms are present and healthy...

It's Sustainable

Wildwood Tree Farm is a place where sustainable, selective logging is practiced. I must emphasize *sustainable*. Selective is not good enough.

I've met loggers who claim to do selective logging. This usually means that the best trees will be selected for cutting and the rest left with little consideration for regrowth or future production, certainly not for aesthetics.

Sustainable means "to sustain" or, to keep the trees in production, sustaining the level of growth of the stand and never over-cutting that growth. These 136 acres grow between 500-700 board feet per acre per year which gives a potential harvest of 68,000 board feet of timber each year. During the 1985-89 period, Wildwood grew 270,000 board feet of timber. When completing my ninth cut in January 1990, I had removed the 270,000 board feet. I count anything over six inches in the growth factor, therefore I must include any wood used for fence posts, firewood, and shakes, along with the milled timber. This is sustainable forestry management. Really, in effect, sustainable *is* selective. A forest which is utilized economically cannot be sustained without being selective. The two are interdependent.

"These 136 acres grow between 500-700 board feet per acre per year which gives a potential harvest of 68,000 board feet of timber each year."

Harvesting of the trees can be done in cycles or continuously as long as the proper percentage is taken. I never cut over the annual growth rate, as that breaks into the "bank account" of the tree farm. It may sound like business financing, but consider the forest the "bank account," the annual growth the "interest." The "interest" is converted into the products which are removed from the forest, but the "account" is left standing. I have now learned to leave five percent of my "interest," or annual growth, to decay and rot on the forest floor, a reinvestment in the soil, a reinvestment for the future.

Unfortunately, in British Columbia, the big companies have been allowed to over-cut, abandoning any idea of sustaining. The Department of Forestry claims that in 1988 the forests grew 74 million board feet during the year. The cut during that year was 90 million. I have heard that the more correct figure is 108 million. Is there any worse "deficit financing" than that?

The tree farm is a garden. The produce comes out of a garden every year. My "produce" comes out every five years. The only difference between the garden and the tree farm is time; time which allows the growth to become marketable without the destruction of the forest.

In order to keep the woodlot sustainable, it is necessary to understand certain fundamentals to have healthy, happy, and productive trees. These fundamentals I follow on Wildwood Tree Farm. I know the annual growth of the trees. I understand species-value according to the land and terrain. I thin for light and growth to encourage the proper canopy. I let resceding occur naturally. I must take care of the soil, making sure enough woody debris is returned; and I consider carefully the factors of road building and erosion. I provide myself with a good income in terms of time and investment.

The basic tools needed to operate a tree farm, or woodlot, are minimal compared to other businesses. The common denominator for good sustainable logging is to work *with* nature, using good, common sense. I have a double-bladed axe, one side for chopping at ground level (which may dull the blade), the other side, which is always sharp for use on the trees. I have a power saw that is comfortable to handle and I know the fundamentals of using one. It is not a toy, but a wonderful tool that must be handled with care.

Walking through Wildwood I have learned to observe the growth and well-being of the trees by the length and color of the leaves, and the condition of the bark. In forestry, the learning never stops.

Soil: The Real Resource

A forest depends on the quality of its soil. The soil consists of many things: the organic matter and plant nutrients; the sub-soils underneath which provide the trees with anchorage and mineral intake; the bacteria and micro-organisms; the fungi and the bugs and critters that aerate the soil. It is a balanced entity, so that if you destroy that balance, you're going to be in trouble...

Leaving biodegradable waste on the forest floor is the most effective way for improving soil. The best biodegradable waste is that which comes from the trees themselves, thereby ensuring that nothing is introduced which will upset the ecosystem. Branches, leaves, needles and log sections should be left to rot. After a cut, I care for the soil by allowing forest litter (branches, unusable parts of the trunk, rotten wood) to go back to the forest floor. Organic material on the surface indicates how quickly decomposition is happening. However, if there is more than 10 cm. of organic materials (often true in swampy sites) tree growth will be slow.

The burning of slash is the worst crime perpetrated against the forest soil. The average soil building rate in North America is one-eighth of an inch every hundred years. If a human-set fire is burned over this, it destroys the accumulation of many centuries of topsoil. It is the topsoil that grows the trees. The subsoil provides the anchorage. If the topsoil is destroyed by fire or scarifying with heavy equipment, causing erosive water run-off, the potential for growing a new forest is lost. Retrogression then takes place and only the primitive forms of plant life grow, such as mosses and lichens. The damage of human-set fires is very great...

In working Wildwood's forest, I planned the roads to protect the soil. Road planning is as important to the woodlot as a foundation is to a house. If the roads are well constructed and not over-used, damage is minimal and accessibility a real asset.

Roads are necessary to extract forest products, but if built incorrectly, the drainage and erosion caused by fast-tracking water completely alters the nature of the forest area. For example, cedar, which desires a considerable amount of moisture, could find its roots too dry because of altered drainage; Douglas fir, in the way of a large amount of run-off, could "drown." The combination of clearcutting and road building contribute enormously to the erosion of soil.

Selective sustainable forestry results in a tremendous saving in road costs. Due to repeated use of the same roads, the amortization goes down with every cut. By the end of my ninth cut, the 1.25 miles of main lead has cost 29 cents per foot. Future cuts will further reduce this cost...

The Essential Ingredient

The essential ingredient in effective woodlot management is time—a long-term perspective and a day-to-day participation in a living landscape that evolves over decades and even centuries. Good woodlot management demonstrates viable alternatives to the devastation of the current forestry practices in British Columbia where timber management has been for short term economic benefits based on the dogma of clear-cut and replant...

"Boardroom foresters cut for the product without respect for the life of the forest. The sustainable selective method is the opposite..."

Alternative woodlot management, as conducted at Wildwood, challenges ingrained ideas. The telescoping of forest productivity into a time frame for boardroom economics is replaced with a continual growing forest. The boardroom's cut and plant mandate is threatening not only the life of our forests, but also our social and economic well-being. Businesses judge success by "net worth." Clear-cutting reduces the net worth of a forest to zero. If that forest was old growth, it will be several hundred years at best before the original value can be obtained, several hundred years not considered on the balance sheet of the company boardroom. Alternative woodlot management understands the time-frame of a forest.

So far, management of our forests has been in the hands of those who do not recognize the forest as an ecosystem of all ages and species which are interdependent. *We too* are dependent upon this ecosystem for clean water and air which tree plantations do not supply. Boardroom foresters cut for the product without respect for the life of the forest. The sustainable selective method is the opposite, enhancing the use of the forest and maximizing the value of the product through marketing...

The management of Wildwood contrasts strongly with the cornrow, industrial-agricultural style of tree farming. Trees for marketing are selected from a diverse natural system of hardwoods and softwoods, retaining all ages within the stand. Here is a forest profitability harvested without compromising the aesthetics of the forest environment. By maintaining such a balanced, healthy landscape, there are still abundant populations of native wildlife; eagles, pileated woodpeckers, owls, deer and a multitude of other creatures in their own habitat.

In understanding that Wildwood is an ecosystem, it is also understood that it is part of a larger ecosystem, the planet. Humans are not separate from that ecosystem. We are part of it and our lives depend on its health. It produces all life, including human.

17

Land Trusts: An Alternative To Land Ownership

Betty Didcoct

A fundamental feature of industrial economies is their relationship to the land. Deeply-ingrained in modern ways of viewing land is that it is a commodity to be bought and sold on the open market, like any other. But this view is in large part responsible not just for the alienation that the people of the industrialized world feel from nature, but also for the care-less attitude toward the Earth that can rationalize its continuing degradation beyond all "Earth-reasonable" limits, to feed the appetite of the Megamachine.

The need for land reform, therefore, is not just limited to dictatorships in some far-off "under-developed" countries. It is first and foremost a requirement for the kind of deep structural change required in the polity of North America and Europe. As Betty Didcoct from the Pacific Northwest explains, the land trust movement is a first step along the road to a profound re-evaluation of our economic relationship with nature.

As the white people moved west in North America, they brought with them the concept of *owning* the land. With this basic notion came two attitudes, both unknown to the Native Americans: first, seeing land as a commodity to be bought and sold; and second, seeing humans as having the right to dominate development of the land without regard for the future health of the land or the other living forms inhabiting the land.

More and more of our decisions about land use and development became solely economic decisions. Land became something to build on, extract from, subdivide; pave, cut up and clear off. It was our resource, here to serve our purposes, to be exploited for our immediate gain. Little attention was given to how the impact of our presence affected the land (or us, for that matter), in the long term.

Fortunately, we are starting to wake up. We are beginning to see that the true economics of land relates more to the wealth which it provides to our grandchildren rather than ourselves. We are beginning to see that having the dollar as the bottom line for decisions about land use does not make as much sense, ultimately, as having the health of the land as the bottom line. We have recognized the devastating effects our domination has had on the land.

How can we translate these insights into effective land reform? It is no easy task. The lessons learned from our habits of dominating land are deeply ingrained and slow to pass away. We face barriers every step of the way because so much of our economic structure is based on the speculative value of the land.

Beyond Traditional Land Ownership

The land trust movement in North America has begun to make a small dent by putting land into legal forms other than traditional ownership. People use land trusts for many different purposes. For some, the interest is to preserve land in wilderness—protected from the impact of people. For others there are unique qualities of land which should be protected. For some, the economic considerations of land are important issues to deal with. Still others want to explore how to re-create a sustainable relationship between people and the land.

A land trust is a non-governmental, usually non-profit, sometimes charitable, organization which is concerned in some way with the protection of land. Land trusts seem to fall into three basic types: conservation trusts, economic trusts, and stewardship trusts.

The main focus of a *conservancy* land trust is to preserve land which has some unique aspect—marsh land, endangered plant or animal species, scenic or agricultural value, wildlife habitat, historic value, etc. Generally the land is protected by conservation easements which give guidelines for the future care of the land. Conservation easements are legal restrictions placed on the land title to prevent the current owners or any future owners from developing the land without the agreement of the trust. The conservancy trust holds these rights to guard against the loss of the unique aspect of the land which it was charged with protecting.

A land trust set up with the intent to remove land from the speculative market and make it available at a cost less than the usual mortgage payment has an *economic* relationship to the land as its main focus. Generally, these trusts are called Community Land Trusts (CLT). The

CLT usually owns the land and grants long term renewable leases (i.e. 99 years) to those who will actually live on the land. Because of the long lease, the tenants have the security and use rights normally associated with ownership. CLTs can accomplish the lower "lease" fee by either acquiring the land by purchase or donation (in some cases CLTs are charitable organizations), carrying a long term mortgage with lower monthly payments, or raising capital by issuing shares of "non-voting preferred stock" backed by the land.

"...so much of our economic structure is based on the speculative value of the land."

Stewardship land trusts work to support a mutually nurturing, long term *relationship* between people and land —a blending of the needs of the people with the needs of the ecosystems. People become *stewards* of the land. What does it mean to be a steward? Long term "living with the land," with sensitivity, with a goal of making the land more fertile and healthy than its original state are the hallmarks of a good steward. The concept of stewardship sees people as more than caretakers—an idea which can keep the human in a controlling, dominating role. A steward's attitude is one of cooperation and interdependence; to enhance both the quality of life for the people and for the land. A stewardship trust works to develop land use plans which take into account as much information about the land as possible—the soil, water, sun exposure, slope, drainage, wildlife habitat, vegetation, etc. as well as human information: historical use, existing use, potential use, views, sacred spots, etc. Stewardship principles are developed to place on the title as easements, giving guidance to the management of the land. The land trust gives the long term context for management even if the stewards change.

These three classifications are not mutually exclusive of one another. For example, the CLT may have a strong desire to see the lease holders as stewards of the land, working with the land in a way which will preserve or enhance its potential for the generations to come. This philosophy can be reflected in the conditions of the lease agreements which establish perameters for the leasees' work with the land. Likewise, the stewardship trust might be working toward economic arrangements with the stewards of the land to make the cost of occupancy more available to a wider range of people.

Shaking The Foundations

How can you go about setting up a land trust? As an individual? As a group of concerned people within your community? The concept of a land trust pre-supposes an outside organization which will hold guardianship over the intentions for which the trust is created. This means that there must be an entity created which draws people who will maintain its purposes and intents.

As an individual: If you have a piece of land which has some unique quality which you feel needs to be preserved, then you might be interested in donating, or possibly selling, a conservation easement (which means giving up some development potential of the land in the future) to a land trust already established in your area. If no such organization exists (most often the case), then you might look to see if others in your community, who have similar attitudes about land preservation, might be willing to join with you to start a land trust.

As a group of concerned people within your community: If there is a group of people who see some particular area or piece of land in your community which, if sold or developed would significantly destroy the quality of life for the residents of the community, it is very possible to create your own land trust. This group could then actively pursue raising money to acquire the land or raising public sentiment so the land (or more likely an easement on the land) might possibly be donated to the land trust. Establishing a new group takes a lot of energy and commitment, but can be very rewarding.

To really get at some of the issues of major land reform, we will shake the very foundations of our economic system. The land trust movement is creating some alternatives which can develop and move along beside our current speculative system. The legal structures we have developed to protect land will not make any difference if we don't make fundamental changes in the philosophies and belief structures which guide us in the ways we relate to the land. But changing attitudes toward land are beginning to emerge. We have made a start.

(For further information, write: TIES Canada,101-5810 Battison Street, Vancouver, B.C. V5R 5X8; or TIES U.S.A., 1420 N.W. Gilman #2346, Issaquah, WA 98027.)

18

Living Machines: Transforming Cape Cod's "Septage"

An interview with John Todd, by David Cayley

Technological optimists regard the global environmental crisis as soluble by technical means, through the discovery of technologies and techniques frequently not yet invented. More often than not, such "techno-fixes" create problems additional to the ones they were designed to solve, resulting in a vicious downward spiral. Characteristic of the techno-fix mentality is a narrowly-focussed view of "the problem:" designing twin-hulled oil supertankers, for example, as a solution to oil spills instead of thinking beyond the dubious ecological merit of transporting oil thousands of miles through dangerous seas. Doing without oil altogether might well be a better answer to the redefined problem. The latter approach might more properly be the one expected of a deeper green commitment to the future.

John Todd brings a new wide-focussed slant to such issues. He calls himself an ecological designer. He believes that the future of civilization lies in living machines, assemblies of organisms that do the work now done by polluting mechanical machines. He began his work in the late '60s as a founder of the New Alchemy Institute, a pioneer in ecological technologies. Today he directs the Center for the Protection and Restoration of Waters, dedicated to using ecological knowledge to solve the problems of water pollution and toxic waste disposal. Here he talks to Toronto writer and broadcaster, David Cayley, in an interview first aired on the Canadian Broadcasting Corporation Radio "Ideas" series.

David Cayley: Harwich, Massachusetts, May 1, 1990. It's a festive occasion. While a steel band plays in the background, the citizens of Harwich circulate amongst large, translucent, cylindrical tanks full of algae, snails, fish and numerous plants. The tanks contain "septage," the toxic, highly concentrated output of septic tanks. But there is no smell and the building, under its gossamer greenhouse roof, is bright and vibrant with life. The occasion is the opening of the Harwich Solar Aquatics Septage Treatment Facility.

The new plant is located in a place only a seagull could love—the back end of the Harwich dump. It's the work of John Todd and his associates, the second such facility they've now completed. Its purpose, as Todd told the opening day crowd, is to treat a type of waste that's difficult to treat with chemical and mechanical technologies—septage.

John Todd: This particular sludge is extremely concentrated. It's some 30 to 100 times more concentrated than ordinary sewage, so it's very, very difficult to treat. This material also has in it, because of our bad household practices, a number of heavy metals and toxic materials which are in themselves carcinogens. So the idea here is, without the use of hazardous chemicals in the treatment process, to purify these compounds, to try and break up these carcinogens that get into our water, using organisms that have this capability, and to try and shunt metals out of the water stream, using organisms which have this particular talent. And so inside this building are probably over 1,000 species of different kinds of organisms, each of which are working in a constellation to accomplish a task that no single one or small group of organisms could ever do. That's the reason why it's called ecological engineering.

"Ecological engineering is really bringing together organisms from the wild and putting them into a new, contained environment to do some of the work for society."

Ecological engineering is really bringing together organisms from the wild and putting them into a new, contained environment to do some of the work for society. In the case here, the work is purifying the wastes. So, in a sense, ecological engineering and solar aquatics are really miniaturizing in a high light environment the processes that take place naturally in lakes and streams, and doing so under controlled conditions so that we can in fact effect something in a matter of days, say ten days here, that would normally take months in the wild.

David Cayley: The town of Harwich is on Cape Cod, which is essentially a big sand bar extending off the coast of Massachusetts, south of Boston, like a crooked finger. There are few sewer systems on the Cape, which means that most wastes are hauled to the town dumps in tank trucks, called "honey wagons," and then dumped into holding ponds or septage lagoons. Below these ponds is the large lens of groundwater which is the Cape's water supply, between them only the Cape's quick-draining, sandy soils. The problem is obvious. But now Harwich has a solution. It's a result of the town's own political initiative, and this is what is most gratifying to John Todd. He's been engineering elegant ecological solutions to contemporary problems for twenty years. Now local communities are starting to get interested. The road to the Harwich dump began in the late '60s, when Todd, his wife and colleague Nancy, and biologist Bill McLarney started the New Alchemy Institute. Medieval alchemy was the precursor of modern science. New Alchemy was to be the harbinger of a new science.

New Alchemy began in southern California in the late '60s and was relocated to Cape Cod, where it still prospers, in 1970. There, the Todds and their colleagues began to pose the questions that would eventually produce a whole new family of technologies.

John Todd: One of the first questions we asked was how could we, in a very small space, using renewable sources of energy and ecological cycles, produce the food needs of a small group of people. In order just to accomplish those ends in a small space, we had to immediately develop integrated systems. And so we had a pond, for example, inside a small solar greenhouse-like structure. The pond was in that structure in order to absorb enough radiant energy so we didn't have to heat it with fossil fuels, much the way the ocean provides the climate for planet Earth. We did the same thing. We began to use that body of water which was providing the thermal storage and the thermal buffer for aquaculture, and that married ancient Chinese methods of polyculture, which we got from the Orient, with modern ecological knowledge, combined with the idea of introducing a lot of light. Out of that grew the whole area of work called solar aquatic accuaculture.

In some cases, on the surface of the water we would be growing foods. To do that, we began to study the ancient Mayan floating agriculture and bring that into our thinking. And then, because we were growing fish in this small space, we couldn't use any agricultural poison—it would kill the fish—so we had to find ecological methods of pest control. For example, we had to look at predator-prey relations, a subject dear to the heart of academic ecology, and find those beneficial organisms to fit in our small habitats. And then we began to start working with wind energy or moving water for providing electricity, for a whole variety of things, and then began to start designing sytems based on pulses. For example, wind doesn't blow all the time. So if you have a fish farm powered by a windmill, you have to design it so that it can cope with natural pulses, which is the opposite of the Western mechanistic point of view, which is to just sock to it a continuous source of electricity and maintain a steady state system. We decided that working with pulses might be beneficial, and so we started to study pulse-like environments, like a tidal marsh, and asked marshes—what are you doing and how do you do it? We want to do it, too. That knowledge from mangroves, tidal marshes and things like that became incorporated into the thinking.

David Cayley: Out of this early research came a new type of building called a bioshelter, a building capable of regulating its own climate, producing food and recycling its own wastes. Both John and Nancy Todd were born and grew up in Canada, though they've made their lives and careers in the U.S..

One of the first projects that Todd got off the ground was a solar aquatics waste treatment facility for the city of Providence, Rhode Island, not far from his own home on Cape Cod. Like the Harwich facility described earlier, it's a greenhouse structure, containing engineered marshes and lines of translucent tanks where an amazing variety of plants, microbes and marine creatures purify Providence's wastes. Unlike conventional secondary treatment plants, it uses little energy, no hazardous chemicals and produces no toxic by-products. It was opened in July of 1989 and has continued in successful operation since. John Todd toured me around.

"What comes in at one end of the building is raw, untreated industrial sewage from an industrially-based city, and what you see here is water leaving the building pure and transformed from that original state."

John Todd: We're right in the bowels of Providence, Rhode Island, in the center of the most industrial district of the city. To our immediate east are 63 million gallons of partially treated sewage roaring out into Narragansett Bay. Right in the middle of all this, we have a gossamer-like greenhouse structure, and inside that structure is a water garden. If you were to walk into it, you would see ginger and flowers and watercress and fish and snails and clams and herbs and spices. What comes in at one end of the building is raw, untreated industrial sewage from an industrially-based city, and what you see here—the sound of falling water, right here—is water leaving the building pure and transformed from that original state.

We're now inside the first chamber. The raw material sewage is quickly being transformed into these great vats of algae, and then the algae, in turn, are kept in check by these large grazing populations of snails. All these dots over the surface are snails, which really are the sheep and the cattle of the aquatic realm. The organic material bursts up to the surface, the surface is grabbed on to by the roots of these microscopic floating plants here, and in there is where the bacteria reside that do the waste treatment. Then the snails themselves consume the bacteria that treat the waste, and so begins the basis of the food chain. These mountains of foam that you see coming off are the various surfactants and wastes from restaurants and wastes from households, the soaps and other types of things. In those foams, again, there are algae and bacteria and other organisms that also continue to do the treatment process. At the very beginning, you can see higher plants floating on the surface. That's a tropical plant, the water hyacinth, and during the summer months here, it is just a mass of orchid-like flowers. The contradiction between the treating of waste and the aesthetic is one that we find very interesting and somewhat ironic.

We've now moved into the second and largest room inside the solar aquatic waste treatment greenhouse. Basically, this second stage in the treatment process mimics exactly the strategies a salt marsh uses, which is a period of drying and a period of wetting. So that, for half of the day in here, the marshes dry out, and that allows air to penetrate down into the system, and then the other half of the marsh—they're all in parallel, there are eight of them here—the other half of the system is wet and becomes anaerobic, doing one type of purification process. The side over here, which is dry, becomes aerobic and is prepared to do another kind. As you can see, this is an eclectic marsh, if ever there was one! We have the umbrella plant, which I think originated in North Africa; we have the eucalyptus, which is from Australia; and we have the scirpus, the bulrushes, from North America, three or four species—these are all intertwined in this system to produce a polyculture, with each plant having different depths and different functions. Some remove organic carcinogens, actually physically break them up. Some of these other plants entrap heavy metals and lock them up rather than allow them into the environment, getting them out of the water so that they're not re-released into the bay. Now what we do with these heavy metals varies, depending on the plants that they get in. If it's a tree, a long-lived tree, then we like to find trees that concentrate metals in the stems and roots, and we can lock up these metals then for centuries or many, many years because they're planted out after they start life in this building to become landscape trees afterwards. That's an important side of the story. Other plants take up heavy metals, like the tiny floating plants, and those are composted before they reach hazardous levels in the plant, so that they can be re-used on the landscape. But the metal levels are low enough that it doesn't cause long range degradation of the external environment.

The third strategy that we use here is unique, and that is because this is an industrial city and the backbone of this city is in fact the jewellery industry. What we're attempting to do here is try and find plants which are called hyperaccumulators: plants that actually try and mire specific species of metals out of the water and concentrate them so that they could be re-used as ore grade. We have a long term project to try and study just this phenomenon and see if we can find metal mining plants that are happy to live in water or in wet marsh-like environments.

David Cayley: Because the sewage you're getting contains significant amounts of precious metals?

John Todd: Yes, all of the precious metals are here. I don't think we measure for gold, but we measure for silver, of course, and then there's cadmium and mercury and lead and things like that. It's all in the sewers of the city and it's very erratic. Sometimes there's very little and then all of a sudden there'll be a big spike, and that tells us that one of the factories has done a discharge into the sewers of the town.

"Because it's beautiful, because it doesn't stink, we now have the opportunity for the first time to disagregate the problem of waste. So that each neighborhood or each community could have its own facility."

Then as we walk toward the final treatment process, the actual diversity of plants and animals increases. Now we come into an area where we have crayfish and clams and more and more different species of plants. It's a tiny aquatic fern floating here that produces that carpet-like mat. Then, of course, there's the ubiquitous watercress in this system—the work horses in here.

The final stage is basically again an engineered marsh, but it's really a polishing marsh. The idea is to remove the last of the fine particles. The other thing that's very important in this phase of the process is to have plants in the polishing which are powerfully antibiotic. Most bulbs are antibiotics, and that's one of the reasons why they store so well and don't rot so easily if they're kept relatively dry. So you'll see a fair number of bulb plants in the system. Things like irises and others tend to be very good this way. Finally, it passes down through the fine crushed gravel filter and then leaves the building as clean water, roughly four days after it entered here.

The facility we're looking at here can treat the needs of about 150 households. It's roughly 11 metres by 40 metres in length, and if we were to do all of the city of Providence, we're looking at an area of roughly 120 acres. That's comparable to the acreage that is currently used by the city to treat their waste to secondary standards, and this facility is treating to advanced wastewater standards. So when it comes to space, these new, light-driven, ecologically based processes are space competitive. The opportunity to treat the whole city in one place is there.

But the other side of the coin, which I think is very important, is that because it's beautiful, because it doesn't stink, we now have the opportunity for the first time to disaggregate the problem of waste. So that each neighborhood or each community could have its own facility, each neighborhood or community could use its own by-products, the trees, the various flowers and things like that, to enhance the environment, so that these facilities could become epicenters for the whole landscaping of areas, including cities. That way, if anything goes wrong here at this plant, we have somewhere between 60 and 100 million gallons a day going into the Narragansett Bay, one of the great bodies of water in this part of the world. Whereas if each plant served a community, there would never be that kind of disaster.

David Cayley: How about the cost of doing it?

John Todd: We've addressed the issue of cost in two ways. The first is if we're dealing with a very concentrated waste, like septage, which is 30 to 100 times more concentrated than sewage and hard to treat conventionally, then we are far more cost effective than any other technology. When it comes to sewage, we don't yet know our costs in relation to other facilities. It looks to us as though, for the price of an ordinary secondary treatment plant, we can build an advanced wastewater treatment facility—we are modestly more cost effective in the dilute waste or sewage waste area.

David Cayley: The knowledge you've spent half a lifetime acquiring must be at play here. Is this a kind of coming to fruition of the knowledge that goes right back to the beginning of New Alchemy?

John Todd: There is no question that this is a fruition, a coming of age. I have enough experience with different kinds of organisms and different animals and the way they work together in concert, that I've actually reached the point in my life where I can start talking about something quite revolutionary and quite new: the concept of a living machine. And a living machine is in fact an ecologically engineered technology that uses wide varieties of organisms to carry out the work of society. I can see the same kind of knowledge being used to produce foods without any environmental degradation, perhaps let's say environmental enhancement. I can see the same kind of living machines producing fuels for our automobiles. I can see these same types of living machines regulating our climates, both heating and cooling and air purification. So in areas of waste, food, fuel and even architecture, one can begin to see living machines which are contained in these gossamer-like environments with light penetrating everywhere, functioning as the work horses. In a sense, for the first time in the history of technology, we're able to actually miniaturize the process of production and recycling. Some of these can be made to last for centuries, unlike mechanical or chemical engines. The overall systems can go on forever. They're self-replicating, self-repairing. They have all of the capabilities of machines, except they have attributes that machines don't have, hence the name "living machines."

I think we're on the threshold of something really fundamental. Carried one step further, in fact, we are even beginning to talk about the idea, both in eastern Europe and in New York City, of actually designing intelligent buildings that carry out all of the support attributes using living machines.

"John Todd's eye has always been for structure. He wants to redesign society so its structure resembles the structure of the living world."

David Cayley: Ten years ago, in a book called *Tomorrow Is Our Permanent Address*, John and Nancy Todd drew a distinction between the structure of a system and its coefficients. An automobile is a structure, the fuel efficiency of its engine a coefficient. Tinkering with coefficients is the easiest and least threatening way to approach environmental problems. Improving the fuel efficiency of cars without challenging the structure of transportation is a good example. Using energy to recycle something that needn't have been produced in the first place would be another.

John Todd's eye has always been for structure. He wants to redesign society so its structure resembles the structure of the living world. In living systems, each part is linked to the whole but retains a certain independence. This is what gives the system its resilience and adaptability. In contemporary social structures, that element of autonomy is missing. Analyze even your household economy and you'll probably find yourself linked into scores of unstable, ecologically destructive, politically questionable supply lines extending right around the world. Living machines are John Todd's answer, a way of making civilization continuous with nature by designing as nature designs. One of John Todd's inspirations in this work has been the Gaia hypothesis:, the idea that the Earth, as a whole, is self-regulating. Gaia, he thinks, is the framework in which ecological engineering finally makes sense.

John Todd: The whole notion of the Earth as alive is ancient. When it becomes part of the consciousness of people, then their place on Earth changes dramatically. My sense is that economies built on ecology will allow people to live and believe in one system, whereas now you can believe in Gaia and a single, wonderful manifest ecology, but how do you act on that belief, how do you live on that belief? I think sometime in the future, the living and believing can come into harmony. The Gaian idea is coming around at the right time to provide a broad mantle under which people change their values and the way they work, and their relationship with other living things, not just with each other. That's my source of optimism.

19

Free Cities At Work

David Morris

Business takes place in a larger context than the individual transactions that occur when you buy or sell something, and often this context is an outgrowth of business relations defined by the city. But the sprawling conurbations of North America are regarded usually with dismay and apprehension by those wishing to "green" them. However, cities as they existed in medieval times were far from being the alienating concrete jungles of today. Rather, they represented a flowering of human social organization, hotbeds of invention and enterprise. Significantly, their operations were highly socialized: prices, debts and the quality of goods made were overseen by the whole community, which was responsible for what that city produced, and how.

If we were able to recreate the conditions under which such cities flourished on, say, a neighborhood scale, we would be taking a giant step in revolutionizing not only the way we do business, but the way in which we conceive of the basics of economics: production, distribution, marketing and consumption. Furthermore, it would offer an opportunity to re-introduce the idea of a commonly-defined and shared ethic into the marketplace. Together these elements perhaps constitute the very basis of green business as it might most ideally be envisaged. David Morris, a writer and director of the Institute for Local Self-Reliance in Washington, D.C., leaves us with an image from history that might serve as inspiration for a truly green future.

With a unanimity which seems almost incomprehensible, fortified villages rose against the lord's castle, defied it first, attacked it next, and finally destroyed it," Petr Kropotkin wrote 100 years ago in his classic *Mutual Aid*. "The movement spread from spot to spot, involving every town on the surface of Europe, and in less than a hundred years free cities had been called into existence on the coasts of the Mediterranean, the North Sea, the Baltic, the Atlantic Ocean, down to the Fjords of Scandinavia…in the plains of Russia, Hungary, France and Spain."

A thousand years after the free city movement conquered Europe, it remains a beacon for those who believe that cooperative communities based on shared responsibility can be both purposeful and prosperous, democratic and dynamic.

Medieval cities were organized around territory and occupation. All households were united into small territorial unions—the street, the parish, the section. Neighborhoods of 10,000 or so were responsible for controlling crime and meting out punishment. They elected their judges and priests, and formed their own militia.

Workers belonged to guilds, which governed their members and, through them, the economy of cities, with a code of conduct that mixed professional and personal responsibility. In one typical code, if a member fell dangerously ill, two brethren had to keep watch by his or her bed until he or she was out of danger. In case of death they had to provide for the children. Quarrels among members were settled by the guild. If a town were called to arms, the guild appeared as a separate company under elected commanders.

"Production was a social duty, and a social responsibility. In many cities, the entire city was held responsible for the debts contracted by any one of its merchants."

Medieval economies were not guided by an invisible hand. Third parties, with full access to knowledge about the costs of production, often set prices. Merchants and sailors in one city detailed under oath the first cost of imported goods and the expense of transportation. The mayor of town and two "discreet" men then set the selling price.

Cities commanded that products produced within their jurisdiction be of the highest quality. Wood, leather, or thread used by the artisan must be "right," insisted one ordinance. Bread must be baked "in justice," noted another.

The judges of quality were the worker's colleagues. The guild, not the individual producer, offered the goods for sale in the community. The community, in turn, offered goods to the brotherhood of allied communities and assumed responsibility for their quality. Technical defects reflected poorly on not only the individual worker and the guild, but on the territorial community.

Production was a social duty, and a social responsibility. In many cities, the entire city was held responsible for the debts contracted by any one of its merchants.

Free cities regulated supply and demand, set prices, and enforced a sense of mutual responsibility. Was this a capitalist economy? A socialist economy? Neither. The word that Kropotkin and his followers used to describe it was "anarchy." To many of us that means chaos. To Kropotkin it described a society where decisions are made by those most directly affected, and many small local producers provide the necessary goods and services.

In the middle ages, anarchy produced remarkable results. "In the beginning of the eleventh century the towns of Europe were small clusters of miserable huts, adorned but with low clumsy churches, the builders of which hardly knew how to make an arch," Kropotkin observed. "(T)he arts, mostly consisting of some weaving and forging, were in their infancy; learning was found but in a few monasteries."

Three hundred and fifty years later, the very face of Europe had been changed. "The land was dotted with rich cities, surrounded by immense thick walls which were embellished by towers and gates, each of them a work of art in itself... The crafts and arts had risen to a degree of perfection which we can hardly boast of having superseded in many directions, if the inventive skill of the worker and superior finish of his work be appreciated higher than rapidity of fabrication," said Kropotkin. "The navies of free cities furrowed in all directions the Northern and Southern Mediterranean; one effort more and they would cross the oceans... The methods of science had been elaborated; the basis of natural philosophy had been laid down; the way had been paved for all the technical inventions of which our own times are so proud."

"Free Cities regulated supply and demand, set prices, and enforced a sense of mutual responsibility."

Cities of fewer than 90,000 people—the size of many contemporary urban neighborhoods—became hothouses of invention. One science historian listed the technical advances bequeathed us from these tiny associations of free citizens: paper, printing and engraving, improved glass and steel, gunpowder, clocks, telescopes, the mariner's compass, the reformed calendar, the decimal notation. Algebra, trigonometry, chemistry, counterpoint (an invention equivalent to a new creation of music)."

Five hundred years later, medieval art and architecture continue to inspire us, in part because all art then was public art. "No works must be begun by the commune, but such as are conceived in response to the grand heart of the commune, composed of the hearts of all citizens united in one common will," insisted the Council of Florence. The medieval cathedral was not just a building, but a symbol of the victory of the city, and the skill and cooperativeness of its workers.

Medieval cities lacked the conveniences we now take for granted, but that doesn't mean that their inhabitants' life was bleak. As befits communities governed by workers, a 48 hour workweek was common, a practice not seen again until this century. Parisian workers had 30 holidays. Wages were excellent. In Saxony a building tradesperson could buy three sheep and one pair of shoes with a week's earnings. Today such a purchase would call for a weekly wage of about $150. In fifteenth century Amiens a smithy or mason or carpenter could buy almost 50 pounds of bread on a day's wages. Today's worker would have to take home $300 a week to do the same.

Free cities eventually fell to external and internal forces. Was their transformation into dependencies of nation states inevitable? Murray Bookchin, in his magnificent *The Rise of Urbanization and the Decline of Citizenship*, raises the possibility that confederations of cities rather than nations, could have constituted the next stage of economic evolution. When the Holy Roman Empire invaded Italy and marched against Milan, "Crema, Piacenza, Brescia, Tortona, etc. went to the rescue; the banners of the guilds of Verona, Padua, Vicenza and Trevisa floated side by side in the cities' camp against the banners of the Emperor and the nobles." The following year, 1167, the Lombardy League had begun. By 1226 it encompassed nearly all of the major cities of northern Italy.

In 1384 the Swabian League of German cities proposed to join the Swiss Confederation of cities, forerunner of the powerful Swiss cantons. "Had the Swiss been responsive to these overtures," muses Bookchin, "European history might have taken a very different turn than it did, possibly replacing nationalism with confederalism."

The 500 year reign of free cities teaches us that cooperation can be an effective organizing principle, not only for individual enterprises but for entire societies.